Edexcel GCSE (9–1)
Biology, Chemistry & Physics
Lab Book

Contents

Published by Pearson Education Limited, 80 Strand, London, WC2R 0RL.

Text © Mark Levesley, Penny Johnson, Sue Kearsey, Iain Brand, Nigel Saunders, Sue Robilliard, Carol Tear

Series editor: Mark Levesley

Typeset & illustrated by Tech-Set Ltd, Gateshead

Original illustrations © Pearson Education Limited

Cover design by Peter Stratton

The rights of Mark Levesley, Penny Johnson, Sue Kearsey, Iain Brand, Nigel Saunders, Sue Robilliard, Carol Tear to be identified as authors of this work have been asserted by them in accordance with the Copyright, Designs and Patents Act 1988.

The Publishers would like to thank Allison Court and John Kavanagh for their contributions to the text.

First published 2017

© Pearson Education Ltd 2017. This material is not copyright free.

Cover image: Shutterstock: Sebastian Kaulitzki

All other media © Pearson Education

Pearson Education Limited is not responsible for the content of any external internet sites. It is essential for tutors to preview each website before using it in class so as to ensure that the URL is still accurate, relevant and appropriate. We suggest that tutors bookmark useful websites and consider enabling students to access them through the school/college intranet.

A note from the Publishers: Pearson Education Limited: This resource is based on the March 2016 accredited version of the specification. The worksheets and tests in this resource have not been reviewed or endorsed by Edexcel and should not be considered as being published by Edexcel.

Copies of official specifications for all Edexcel qualifications may be found on the website: www.edexcel.com

While the Publishers have made every attempt to ensure that advice on the qualification and its assessment is accurate, the official specification and associated assessment guidance materials are the only authoritative source of information and should always be referred to for definitive guidance. Pearson examiners have not contributed to any sections in this resource relevant to examination papers for which they have responsibility. Examiners will not use this resource as a source of material for any assessment set by Pearson.

The worksheets and tests are not required to achieve this Pearson qualification. It is not the only suitable material available to support the qualification, and any resource lists produced by the awarding body shall include appropriate resources.

- light microscope

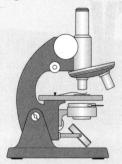

- transparent ruler

- microscope slide and coverslip

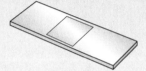

- pipette

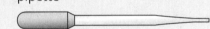

- gloves

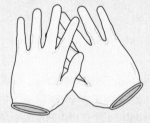

- wooden toothpick/cocktail stick

- sterile wooden spatula/tongue depressor

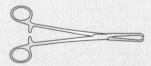

- forceps

- iodine solution in dropping bottle

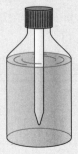

- dimple tile

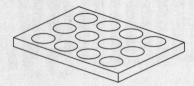

- test tubes

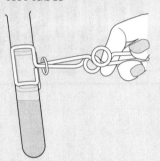

- syringes

- stop clock

- two-holed bung with delivery tube in one hole connected to rubber tubing

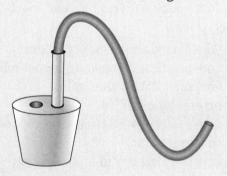

- trough containing water

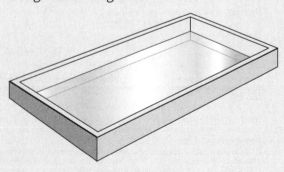

- 100 cm³ conical flask

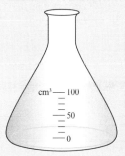

- measuring cylinder

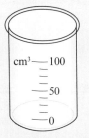

- clamp stand and boss

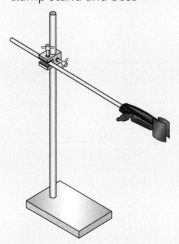

- eye protection

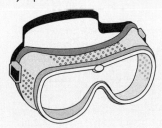

- test tube rack

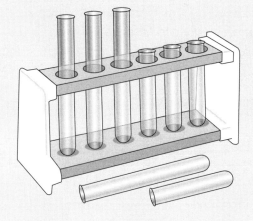

- conical flask with side arm

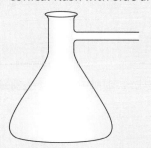

- delivery tube

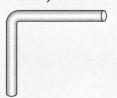

- Bunsen burner

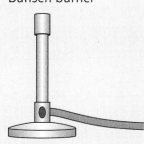

- gauze

- rubber bung with thermometer

- beaker

- tripod

- heat-resistant mat

- Petri dish or watch glass

- evaporating basin

- spatula

- stirring rod

- filter funnel

- filter paper

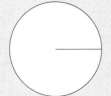

- tongs

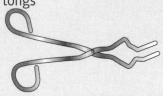

- water bath (set at 50 °C)

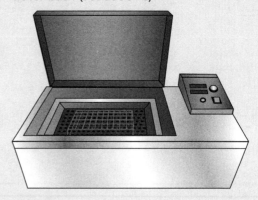

- ±0.1 g balance

- white tile

- trolley

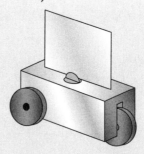

- ramp

- blocks to prop up the end of the ramp

- string

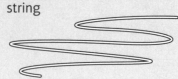

Biology, Chemistry & Physics

- pulley

- masses

- datalogger

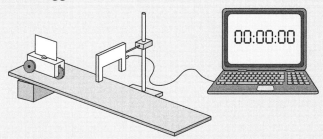

- light gate

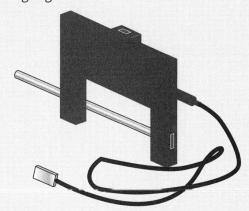

- ripple tank

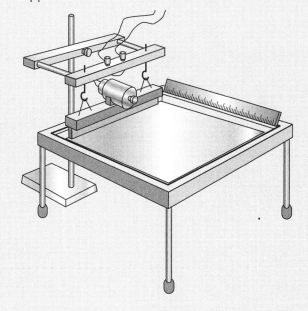

- metre rule

- hammer

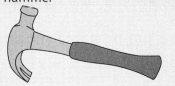

- long metal rod

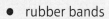

- rubber bands

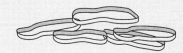

- ray box with single slit

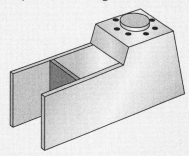

- power supply

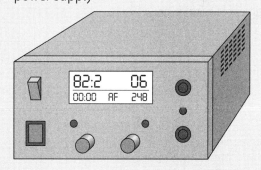

- rectangular glass block

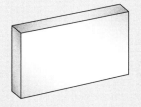

- protractor

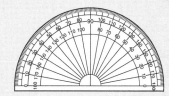

Examining specimens using a microscope and then making labelled drawings of them is a basic skill that you will need in your study of biology. This practical gives you an opportunity to practise this skill.

Your teacher may watch to see if you can:

- handle microscopes and slides carefully and safely.

Method 1: Examining pre-prepared slides of cells

A You will be changing the magnification of your microscope during this section of the practical. Use the box below to record all of your calculations. Set up your microscope on the lowest magnification objective lens. Work out the total magnification and measure the diameter of the field of view (by using the microscope to observe a transparent ruler).

B Put the next most powerful objective lens in place. Work out the magnification and by how much it has increased from the magnification in step **A** (e.g. moving from a ×10 to a ×50 is an increase of 5 times). Now divide the diameter of the field of view from step **A** by the increase in magnification to give you the new diameter of the field of view (e.g. if the field of view in step **A** was 2 mm, then 2 ÷ 5 = 0.4 mm). Do this for each objective lens. Record the total magnification and field of view diameter for each objective lens.

C Now go back to the lowest magnification objective lens and observe a prepared slide.

D Use higher magnifications to observe the cells. Estimate the sizes using your field of view diameters.

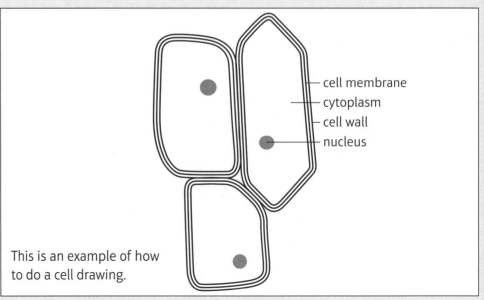

- cell membrane
- cytoplasm
- cell wall
- nucleus

This is an example of how to do a cell drawing.

E Using a sharp pencil, draw 4–5 cells in the box below. There is an example of how to do a microscope drawing in the box on the previous page. Identify and label the cells' parts. Use a ruler to draw your label lines. Write on the magnification. Add any sizes that you have estimated. Have a look for mitochondria (you may not find any as they are very difficult to see).

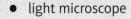
Method 2: Examining your cheek cells

A Using the pipette, add a small drop of water to the slide.

B Stroke the inside of your cheek gently with the wooden spatula. You only want to collect loose cells, so do not scratch the inside of your mouth.

C Use the end of the spatula that has been in your mouth to stir the drop of water on the slide. Place the used spatula in disinfectant.

D Put on gloves and use a pipette to add a small drop of methylene blue stain. This makes cells easier to see.

E Place a coverslip onto the slide at a 45° angle on one edge of the drop. Then use a toothpick to gently lower the coverslip down onto the drop, as shown in the diagram. Avoid trapping air bubbles, which appear as black-edged circles under a microscope.

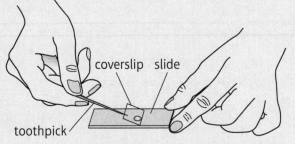

coverslip slide

toothpick

F Touch a piece of paper towel to any liquid that spreads out from under the coverslip.

G Use the lowest magnification objective lens to observe the slide. The nuclei of the cheek cells will be dark blue.

H Use higher magnifications to observe the cells. Estimate the sizes using your field of view diameters.

I Using a sharp pencil, draw 4–5 cells in the box below. Identify and label the cells' parts. Use a ruler to draw your label lines. Write on the magnification. Add any sizes that you have estimated. Have a look for mitochondria (you may not find any as they are very difficult to see).

Apparatus

- light microscope
- lamp
- microscope slide
- coverslip
- methylene blue stain
- pipette
- paper towel
- water
- gloves
- wooden toothpick/ cocktail stick
- sterile wooden spatula/ tongue depressor
- disinfectant

Safety

Handle slides with care.

Anything that you have put into your mouth should be placed in disinfectant after use.

Wear gloves if using stains.

Wear eye protection.

Method 3: Examining onion or rhubarb stem cells

A If you are going to look at onion cells, put on gloves and use a pipette to add a drop of iodine solution to a microscope slide. If you are going to look at rhubarb, add a drop of water to a microscope slide.

B Using forceps, remove a very small piece of the thin 'skin' on the inside of the fleshy part of the onion. It is very thin indeed and quite tricky to handle. Or remove a thin piece of red 'skin' from a rhubarb stem.

C Place the small piece of skin on the drop on the slide.

D Place a coverslip onto the slide at a 45° angle on one edge of the drop. Then use a toothpick to gently lower the coverslip down onto the drop, as shown in the diagram. 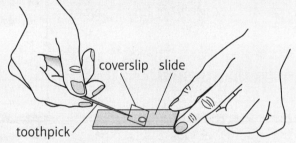 Avoid trapping air bubbles, which appear as black-edged circles under a microscope.

E Touch a piece of paper towel to any liquid that spreads out from under the coverslip.

F Use the lowest magnification objective lens to observe the slide. Then use higher magnifications to observe the cells in more detail. Estimate sizes as you observe.

G Using a sharp pencil, draw 4–5 cells in the box below. Identify the cells' parts and label them. Use a ruler to draw your label lines. Write on the magnification. Add any sizes that you have estimated. Have a look for mitochondria (you may not find any as they are very difficult to see).

Apparatus

- light microscope
- lamp
- microscope slide
- coverslip
- iodine stain
- pipette
- paper towel
- water
- forceps
- wooden toothpick
- piece of onion bulb or rhubarb stem
- gloves

Safety ⚠

Handle slides and microscopes with care.

Wear gloves if using stains.

Wear eye protection.

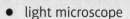
Method 4: Examining pondweed

A Tear off a very small piece of pondweed leaf: a square with sides of up to 2 mm.

B Place the leaf sample onto a microscope slide and add a drop of water.

C Place a coverslip onto the slide at a 45° angle on one edge of the drop. Then use a toothpick to gently lower the coverslip down onto the drop, as shown in the diagram on page 8. Avoid trapping air bubbles, which appear as black-edged circles under a microscope.

D Touch a piece of paper towel to any liquid that spreads out from under the coverslip.

E Use the lowest magnification objective lens to observe the slide.

F Use higher magnifications to observe the cells in more detail. Estimate sizes as you observe.

G Using a sharp pencil, draw 4–5 cells in the box below. Identify the cells' parts and label them. Use a ruler to draw your label lines. Write on the magnification. Add any sizes that you have estimated. If you watch very carefully when you have the cells under a high magnification, you may well see the chloroplasts moving as the cytoplasm moves inside the cells.

Apparatus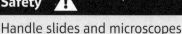

- light microscope
- lamp
- microscope slide
- coverslip
- iodine stain
- pipette
- paper towel
- water
- forceps
- wooden toothpick
- piece of pondweed

Safety ⚠

Handle slides and microscopes with care.

Wear eye protection.

Exam-style questions

1 A microscope is fitted with three objective lenses (of ×2, ×5 and ×10).

   a State what ×2 on a lens means. **(1)**

....

....

   b The microscope has a ×7 eyepiece lens.
      Calculate the possible total magnifications.
      Show your working. **(3)**

....

2 When looking at plant root tissue under a microscope, Jenna notices that about 10 cells fit across the field of view.
   She calculates the diameter of the field of view as 0.2 mm.
   Estimate the diameter of one cell.
   Show your working. **(2)**

....

3 Sasha draws a palisade cell from a star anise plant.
   The cell has a length of 0.45 mm.

   a Sasha's drawing is magnified ×500.
      Calculate the length of the cell in Sasha's drawing. **(1)**

....

   b Sasha adds a scale bar to show 0.1 mm.
      Calculate the length of the scale bar. **(1)**

....

You will be given a range of powdered foods. Use the tests below to identify whether each food contains the substances that the reagents test for.
Use your results to help you identify the foods from the list you are given.
Remember to wipe the spatula and stirrer clean between tests with a paper towel, to prevent cross-contamination.

Your teacher may watch to see if you can:

- follow instructions carefully
- work safely, reducing the risk of harm from hazards.

Iodine test for starch

A Place one spatula of powdered food on a dish.

B Using a dropper, place a few drops of iodine solution onto the food.

C Record the letter of the food and any change in the colour of the solution.

Benedict's test for reducing sugars

D Place two spatulas of powdered food into a test tube. Add about $1\,cm^3$ depth of water to the tube and stir to mix.

E Add an equal volume of Benedict's solution and mix.

F Place the tube in a water bath at about 95 °C for a few minutes.

G Record the letter of the food and the colour of the solution.

Biuret test for protein

H Place two spatulas of powdered food into a test tube. Add about $1\,cm^3$ depth of water to the tube and stir to mix.

I Add an equal volume of potassium hydroxide solution to the tube and stir.

J Add two drops of copper sulfate solution and stir.

K Record the letter of the food and the colour of the solution after a few minutes.

Emulsion test for lipids

L Place two spatulas of powdered food into a test tube.

M Add $2\,cm^3$ of ethanol to the tube. Place a bung firmly in the end of the tube and shake the tube vigorously.

N Allow the contents to settle.

O Pour the liquid from the top of the mixture into a test tube half-filled with water.

P Record the letter of the food and whether the water is cloudy or clear.

Aim

To identify starch, reducing sugars, proteins and lipids in foods.

Apparatus

- eye protection
- water
- measuring cylinder
- spatula
- powdered foods
- paper towels
- test tubes, racks and bungs
- stirrer
- iodine solution in dropper bottle
- Benedict's solution
- potassium hydroxide solution
- copper sulfate solution
- ethanol
- cold water
- water bath at 70 °C

Safety ⚠

Wear eye protection.
Wash any splashes from skin quickly.
Do not taste any of the food substances.
Potassium hydroxide can be harmful to skin and eyes.
Avoid scalding with hot water.

Recording your results

1 Record your results in the table.

Food	Colour at end of ...			
	iodine test	**Benedict's test**	**biuret test**	**emulsion test**
A	Yellow ✓	Orange ✓	Light Green/Yellow	Clear
B	Dark Blue ✓	Green/Blue ✓	Light Blue/Yellow	Clear
C	Yellow ✓	Blue ✓	Purple	Clear
D	Brown ✓	Orange ✓	Dark Yellow	Clear

Considering your results/conclusions

2 Which foods contained:

a starch

> B

b reducing sugar

> D, A, B

c protein

> C

d lipid?

3 Do any of your tests give an indication of how much of a substance a food contains?
Give a reason for your answer.

Yes the reducing sugar test, with Benedicts solution has a multi colour sugle fraction the more reducing sugar the Solution will turn from Blue - Green - Orange

Evaluation

4 Identify any problems you had with this experiment, and explain how the method could be improved to reduce or avoid these errors.

Exam-style questions

1 State which substance is identified in each of the following tests.
   a iodine solution test   (1)

   ....

   b biuret test   (1)

   ....

   c ethanol emulsion test   (1)

   ....

   d Benedict's test   (1)

   ....

2 Describe how you would identify any hazards for each of the tests.   (1)

   ....

   ....

   ....

   ....

   ....

   ....

   ....

   ....

3 Predict the result of each of the following tests. Give a reason for each answer.
   a iodine test of cooked rice   (2)

   ....

   ....

   ....

   b Benedict's test on egg white   (2)

   ....

   ....

   c biuret test on egg white   (2)

   ....

   ....

   d ethanol emulsion test on cheese   (2)

   ....

   ....

   ....

Amylase is an enzyme made in the salivary glands in your mouth and in the pancreas. It catalyses the breakdown of starch into smaller sugar molecules. The iodine test identifies the presence of starch, but does not react with sugar. You will use this test to show how effective amylase is in digesting starch at different pHs.

Your teacher may watch to see if you can:

- work safely
- collect accurate data.

Method

A Drop one drop of iodine solution into each depression of the dimple tile.

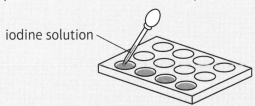

iodine solution

B Measure 2 cm³ of amylase solution into a test tube using a syringe.

C Add 1 cm³ of your pH solution to the test tube using a second syringe. Record the pH of the solution that you are using.

D Using a third syringe, add 2 cm³ starch solution to the mixture and start the stop clock. Use the pipette to stir the mixture.

E After 20 seconds, take a small amount of the mixture in the pipette and place one drop of it on the first iodine drop on the tile. Return the rest of the solution in the pipette to the test tube.

F If the iodine solution turns black, then there is still starch in the mixture and you should repeat step **E** (after 10 seconds). If it remains yellow, then all the starch is digested and you should record the time taken for this to happen.

G If there is time, repeat the experiment using a solution with a different pH.

Prediction

1 Predict at which pH the amylase will digest starch fastest. Explain your prediction. Record your prediction and explanation in the box below.

Aim

To investigate the effect of pH on the rate of digestion of starch by amylase.

Apparatus

- iodine solution in dropping bottle
- dimple tile
- test tubes
- test tube rack
- syringes
- pipette
- amylase solution
- starch solution
- solutions of specific pH
- stop clock

Safety ⚠

Eye protection should be worn.

Recording your results

2 Draw a table in the box below, to present these results clearly.

3 Collect data from all the groups in the class so that you have results for each of the different pHs. If you have more than one result for each pH, calculate a mean time for each one. Record the mean times in the box below.

Considering your results

4 Using the box below, plot a line graph to show the time taken for amylase to digest starch with the different pHs.

5 Look at your graph and use it to describe the effect of pH on the time taken for amylase to digest starch.

6 Suggest a reason for the shape of your graph.

Evaluation

7 Describe any problems you had with carrying out the experiment.

8 Suggest reasons for the problems and how the method could be changed to help reduce the problems.

9 Were any of the results surprising? If so, why?

10 Do you think you have enough results to support your conclusion? Explain your answer.

Exam-style questions

1   Catalase is an enzyme that breaks down hydrogen peroxide into water and oxygen.
    Some students are investigating the effect of pH on this enzyme-controlled reaction by collecting
    the oxygen. One suggestion is to bubble the gas through water and collect it in an upturned
    measuring cylinder full of water. Another suggestion is to collect the water in a gas syringe.

    a Explain which method of gas collection you would use.   **(2)**

    ....

    ....

    b Explain how the students should measure the pH in their investigation.   **(2)**

    ....

    ....

    c The table shows the results from the students' investigation. Draw a graph to display the results.

Time (min)	Volume of O_2 released (cm³)	
	at pH 3	at pH 6
1	1.4	1.6
2	2.7	3.2
3	4.2	5.6
4	5.9	5.7
5	6.6	8.4
6	8.4	10.6

(3)

d Identify the anomalous result and suggest a reason for the error. **(2)**

....

....

....

e Calculate the average rate of reaction (average volume of oxygen produced per minute) at pH 6. **(1)**

....

2 Scientists working on bioleaching are interested in an enzyme called glucose oxidase, which is found in many microorganisms.
The graph shows the results from an investigation into the effect of pH on the rate of activity of glucose oxidase from two different types of bacteria.

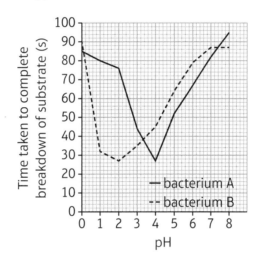

a What is the optimum pH for glucose oxidase from each type of bacterium? **(2)**

....

....

....

b Explain which enzyme is more active at pH 5. **(1)**

....

....

....

c Explain which bacterium might be more useful for bioleaching mine water. **(2)**

....

....

....

Osmosis is the overall movement of water molecules from a region where there are more of them in a particular volume to a region where there are fewer, through a semi-permeable membrane. The cells in a potato contain many substances dissolved in water. The cells are surrounded by cell membranes that are permeable to water. When a strip of potato is placed in a solution, the overall movement of water molecules between the potato cells and the solution will depend on which has the higher concentration of solutes. In this practical, you will investigate osmosis in potato strips in terms of the percentage change in mass of potato in different solutions.

Your teacher may watch to see if you can:

- measure accurately
- work carefully.

Method

A Using the waterproof pen, label each tube with the name of one of the solutions. Place the boiling tubes in the rack.

B Dry a potato strip carefully by blotting it with a paper towel. The potato strips can be removed using a cork borer, as shown in the diagram, or cut using a scalpel. This will have been done for you, before the experiment. Measure its mass on the balance.

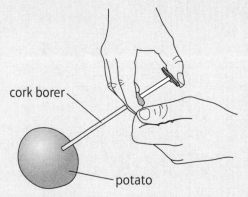

cork borer

potato

C Place the potato strip into one of the tubes. Record the label on the tube and the mass of the strip in your results table (see next page).

D Repeat steps **B** and **C** until all strips have been measured and placed in tubes.

E Carefully fill each tube with the appropriate solution, so that the potato is fully covered. Leave the tubes for at least 15 minutes.

F For each potato strip, use the forceps to remove it from its tube, blot dry on a paper towel and measure its mass again. Record all the masses in the results table.

Prediction

1 For each of the four solutions you will use, predict whether the potato strips will gain mass, lose mass or keep the same mass. Explain your predictions. Record your predictions and explanations in the box below.

....

....

....

....

....

....

....

Aim

To investigate how solution concentration affects percentage change in mass of potato strips due to osmosis.

Apparatus

- four potato strips
- accurate balance
- four boiling tubes and rack (or beakers)
- waterproof pen
- four sucrose solutions: 0%, 40%, 80%, 100%
- forceps
- paper towels

Safety ⚠

Do not drink any of the solutions or eat the potatoes.

Recording your results

2 Complete the first three columns of the table below, labelled 'Solution', 'A' and 'B', with the solution descriptions and your measurements from the experiment.

Solution	**A** Mass of potato strip at start (g)	**B** Mass of potato strip at end (g)	**C** Change in mass (g) = B − A	**D** % change in mass $= \dfrac{C}{A} \times 100\%$

3 Complete column **C** by calculating the change in mass for each potato strip using the formula shown.

4 Complete column **D** by calculating the percentage change in mass for each potato strip using the formula shown.

5 Compare the results for percentage change in mass from all groups in the class for each solution. Identify any results that seem very different from the others (outliers). Try to suggest a reason why they are so different.

....

....

....

....

....

....

....

....

6 Using all results except outliers, calculate a mean value for percentage change in mass for each solution.

7 Draw a suitable chart or graph to show the mean percentage change in the mass of each potato strip on the *y*-axis against the solution description on the *x*-axis.

Considering your results/conclusions

8 Describe the pattern shown in your chart or graph.

9 Explain the pattern shown in your chart or graph, using the word 'osmosis' in your answer.

10 Explain why you calculated percentage change in mass.

11 Explain why calculating a mean value from several repeats of the same experiment is more likely to give a value that can be reproduced by others.

Evaluation

12 Describe any problems that you had with the experiment. Suggest how these could be reduced or avoided to produce better results.

Exam-style questions

1 The table shows the results from an experiment similar to the one described in the method.

Tube	A	B	C	D
Sucrose concentration (g)	0	10	30	50
Mass of potato at start (g)	4.81	5.22	4.94	4.86
Mass of potato at end (g)	4.90	4.96	4.39	3.69

a For each solution, calculate the gain or loss in mass of the potato piece. **(2)**

b For each solution, calculate the percentage change in mass of the potato. **(2)**

c Give a reason for the result from tube A. **(1)**

d Explain the results for tubes B–D. **(2)**

e Use the results to give the possible solute concentration of potato tissue, giving a reason for your answer. **(2)**

....

....

....

f Describe how the method could be adapted to give a more accurate answer to part **e**. **(1)**

....

....

....

2 The graph shows the results of an experiment comparing osmosis in tissue from a halophyte plant and a potato in the same solution.

a Identify, with a reason, which tissue lost water fastest over the first 5 minutes. **(2)**

....

....

b Explain why it lost water faster than the other tissue. **(2)**

....

....

c Calculate the average rate of change in mass over the first four minutes for the potato. **(1)**

....

Microbial cultures (for example, of certain bacteria) are used to study the effects of plant extracts, antibiotics and antiseptics. (Antiseptics are substances used to kill microorganisms on the surface of the body or on equipment.) In this kind of investigation it is important to work aseptically so that the substances are only tested against one organism and the results are not spoiled by other microorganisms.

Your teacher may watch to see if you can:

- work safely and aseptically with microorganisms.

Pouring an agar plate

A Keeping the lid on the Petri dish, turn the dish upside down. Use the pen to draw three sections on the base, as shown in the diagram. Label one section 'control' and the other two sections with the name or concentration of each antibiotic. Add your initials and the date near the edge of the dish. Turn the dish the right way up.

B Light the Bunsen burner and set it to a roaring flame.

C Work in a pair to pour the plate. One student should unscrew the cap of the nutrient agar bottle and quickly pass the glass neck of the bottle through the Bunsen flame, as shown in the diagram. The other student should lift the lid of the Petri dish just enough for the agar to be poured carefully into the dish. Pour in enough agar to half fill the depth of the Petri dish base. Replace the dish lid immediately. Flame the open neck of the agar bottle again before screwing the cap back on.

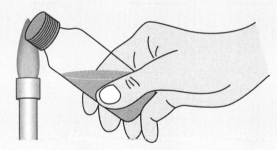

D Leave the agar to solidify.

Making a bacterial plate

E Remove the pipette from its wrapper and do not put it down.

F Unscrew the cap of the bottle of bacterial culture and quickly pass the neck of the bottle through the Bunsen flame.

G Draw a small amount of culture into the pipette then flame the neck of the bottle again and replace the lid.

H Lifting the lid of the Petri dish as little as possible, gently add two drops of culture to the agar. Replace the dish lid and place the pipette in disinfectant.

I Unwrap the spreader and, lifting the dish lid as little as possible, gently spread the culture drops across the agar using a back-and-forwards motion with the spreader.

J Replace the dish lid and place the spreader in disinfectant.

Aim

To investigate the effect of antibiotics on bacteria.

Apparatus

- Petri dish with lid
- screw-top bottle of sterile liquid nutrient agar (keep in water bath until needed) sterilised in an autoclave
- bacterial culture in screw-top bottle
- sterile pipette in wrapper
- sterile spreader in wrapper
- beaker of disinfectant
- two small filter paper discs of different antibiotic concentration or type
- small disc of sterile filter paper
- sticky tape
- marker pen
- forceps
- ethanol (IDA)
- ruler
- Bunsen burner and heat-resistant mat

Safety ⚠

Plates must be taped closed as in the diagram. This allows air in and does not encourage the growth of pathogenic bacteria.

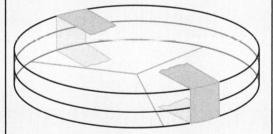

Dispose of all cultures and equipment safely, as instructed by your teacher.

Take care to avoid burning fingers when flaming the neck of an agar bottle.

Avoid touching eyes or skin after handling bacterial cultures. Wash splashes immediately with water.

Wash hands thoroughly before the practical and again before leaving the laboratory.

Ethanol (IDA) is hazardous and highly flammable. Keep away from open flames, except as described in the method.

Adding antibiotic discs

K Sterilise the forceps by dipping them into ethanol then passing them through the Bunsen flame to ignite the ethanol.

L Use the forceps to pick up the sterile filter paper disc. Lift the dish lid just enough so that the forceps do not touch the bacterial layer on the agar in the dish, and carefully place the disc on the section labelled 'control'. Replace the dish lid as quickly as possible.

M Sterilise the forceps as before (step **K**). Then repeat step **L** with one of the antibiotic discs, placing it on the appropriate section of agar. Remember to replace the dish lid as quickly as possible.

N Repeat step **M** with the other antibiotic disc.

O Tape the lid onto your Petri dish with two pieces of tape, as shown in the diagram on the previous page, and invert the dish. Leave it at 20–25 °C for two to three days.

P Look carefully at your dish. **Do not open it**.

Recording your results

1 Measure the diameter of the circle around each disc where there is no bacterial growth, as shown in the diagram opposite.

2 Divide each diameter by 2 to calculate the radius (r) for each circle, and then calculate the area of no bacterial growth using the formula area = πr^2

3 In the space below draw and complete a table to record the area of no bacterial growth for each disc.

diameter of zone labelled as no bacterial growth

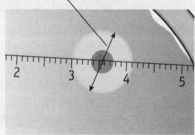

Considering your results/conclusions

4 Explain what your results show about the effect of antibiotics on bacteria.

5 Compare your results with those of other groups.

   a Did other groups get the same results? If not, suggest why not.

   b Explain which of the discs was the most effective at killing bacteria.

Evaluation

6 Suggest a way in which the method could be improved, and give a reason for your suggestion.

7 **a** Identify steps in the method that contributed to working aseptically.

   b Explain the importance of working aseptically in this practical.

Exam-style questions

Three groups of students carried out the experiment described in the method.
Their results are shown in the graph.

How antibiotic concentration affects area of clear space around disc

1 a Describe the difference in results between group 3 and the other groups. **(1)**

....

....

b Suggest a possible reason for the difference. **(1)**

....

....

c Justify your answer to part **b**. **(1)**

....

....

2 Draw a conclusion from the results of groups 1 and 2 shown in the graph. **(2)**

....

....

....

In a different experiment, different antibiotics were tested on a culture of the bacterium *Micrococcus luteus* using a similar method. The results are shown in the table.

Antibiotic	Radius of clear disc (cm)
benzylpenicillin	1.4
methicillin	0.05
streptomycin	1.8

3 Calculate the cross-sectional area of each clear space. **(3)**

....

....

4 Draw a conclusion from the results shown in the table. **(2)**

....

....

....

Introduction

Microscopic algae have cells that contain chloroplasts, like plant leaf cells. The algae can be trapped in jelly balls to make them easier to handle. You will put algal balls in an indicator that changes colour as carbon dioxide levels change. Under normal conditions the indicator is a red colour, but this changes to yellow at higher carbon dioxide concentrations and purple at lower carbon dioxide concentrations.

Your teacher may watch to see if you can:

- follow instructions carefully
- work safely.

Method

A Decide the different distances you are going to use between the algae and the lamp. For each distance you will need one clear glass bottle. You will also need one extra bottle.

B Add 10–15 algal balls to each bottle.

C Add the same volume of indicator solution to each bottle and put on the bottle caps.

D Your teacher will have a chart or a range of bottles showing the colours of the indicator at different pHs. Compare the colour in your bottles with this pH range to work out the pH at the start.

E Set up a heat filter between the lamp and where you will place your tubes. The heat filter is a water-filled bottle or other clear container. Take great care not to spill water near the lamp.

F Cover one bottle in kitchen foil, so that it is in the dark.

G Place your bottles at measured distances from the lamp. Put the bottle covered in kitchen foil next to the bottle that is closest to the lamp.

H Turn on the lamp and time 60 minutes (or longer).

I Compare the colours of all your bottles with those of the pH range bottles (or chart).

J Record the pHs of the solutions in your bottles in a suitable table.

K For each bottle, calculate the change in pH per hour. Add these calculations to your table.

Aim

To find out how light intensity affects the rate of photosynthesis.

Apparatus

- eye protection
- bijou bottles and caps
- beaker of algal balls
- hydrogen carbonate indicator
- lamp and heat filter
- metre rule
- measuring cylinder
- kitchen foil
- clock/stop clock/watch
- plastic forceps/spoon

Safety ⚠

Wear eye protection.

Wash your hands after setting up the experiment.

Avoid touching the hot lamp.

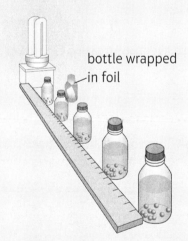

bottle wrapped in foil

Recording your results

1 Record your results in this table.

Distance from lamp to bottle (cm)	pH at start	pH at end	Rate of photosynthesis (change in pH/hour)

Considering your results/conclusions

2 **a** For each bottle, calculate the rate of photosynthesis as the change in pH per hour.

change in pH = pH at end – pH at start

$$rate = \frac{change\ in\ pH}{time\ (in\ hours)}$$

   b Use your calculations to complete the last column of the table on the previous page.

3 Plot your results on a scatter diagram. Plot the variable that you have changed (the independent variable) on the horizontal axis. Plot the rate of photosynthesis on the vertical axis.

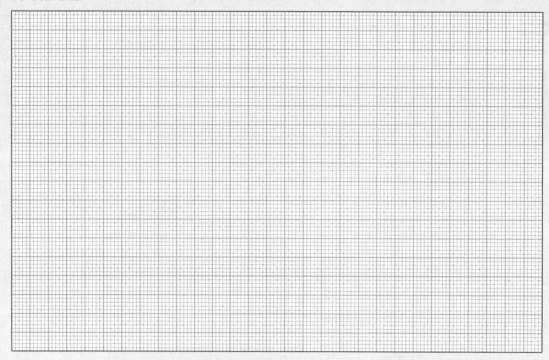

4 **a** Describe the pattern shown on your graph.

....

   b Explain why this pattern is observed.

....

....

Evaluation

5 Fill in the missing words in the sentences below to explain the point of the bottle covered in foil.

The part of an experiment in which the _____ variable is not applied is called the control. A control is used to check that the _____ variable has an effect (and that the effect is not due to another variable). In this experiment, the independent variable is the _____ intensity. The control is the _____ _____. We know that the independent variable has a direct effect on the final pH of the indicator because _____ _____.

30

Exam-style questions

1 Pondweed was placed in a sealed tank of water with an oxygen probe. A datalogger recorded the oxygen concentration in the water. During the experiment, a lamp was switched on and then off again. The results are shown in the graph.

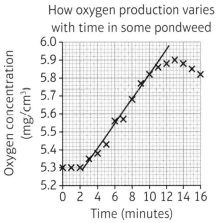

How oxygen production varies with time in some pondweed

a Suggest at what time the lamp was switched on. Give a reason for your answer. **(1)**

....

b Suggest at what time the lamp was switched off. Give a reason for your answer. **(1)**

....

c The slope (or gradient), m, of the line of best fit shows the rate of photosynthesis. Use the graph to calculate the average rate of photosynthesis during this time. Show all your working. **(3)**

....

d The linear relationship shown by the line of best fit can be shown by $y = mx + c$. For this graph, $c = 5.1$. Calculate the concentration of oxygen after 4 minutes 20 seconds. **(3)**

....

e A student thinks the line will be steeper if the light intensity is increased. Explain why the student thinks this. **(3)**

....

....

....

f The idea is tested, but the steepness of the line does not change. Suggest a reason for this. **(2)**

....

....

g State one other possible way of increasing the steepness of the line. **(1)**

....

Scientists are carrying out experiments to find out how human respiration is affected by space travel. They measure respiration using a respirometer which measures the amount of oxygen used, the amount of carbon dioxide produced, or both. You are going to use a simple respirometer.

Your teacher may watch to see if you can:

- work carefully with living organisms
- make accurate measurements.

Method

A Collect a tube with some soda lime in it, held in place with cotton wool. The soda lime absorbs carbon dioxide. Soda lime is corrosive, so do not handle it. The cotton wool is to protect you and the organisms.

B Carefully collect some of the small organisms in a weighing boat.

C Gently shake the organisms out of the container and into the tube.

D Insert the bung and capillary tube, as shown in the diagram.

E Set up a control tube (a tube set up in the same way but without the organisms).

F Place both tubes into a rack in a water bath at a preset temperature. It is best to tilt the rack slightly so that the capillary tubes hang over the side of the water bath at an angle.

G Wait for five minutes to let the organisms adjust to the temperature of the water bath.

H Hold a beaker of coloured liquid to the ends of the capillary tubes, so that liquid enters.

I Mark the position of the coloured liquid in the tubes, and time for five minutes.

J Mark the position of the coloured liquid again, and measure the distance travelled by the liquid.

K Repeat the experiment at different temperatures. Use the same number of organisms each time.

capillary tube   scale

coloured liquid

small organisms

cotton wool

soda lime

Recording your results

1 Record your results in the table below.

Temperature (°C)	Distance moved by the coloured liquid in the tube containing organisms (mm)	Distance moved by the coloured liquid in the control tube (mm)

Considering your results/conclusions

2 Plot your results on a scatter diagram.

3 **a** What was the independent variable in this investigation?

b What was the dependent variable?

c State one control variable described in the method.

d Explain why the variable you gave in **c** needs to be controlled.

e Describe the relationship between the temperature and rate of aerobic respiration.

f Suggest an explanation for this relationship. (*Hint:* think about the effect of temperature on chemical reactions.)

....

....

....

Evaluation

4 The organisms in the tube are respiring aerobically.

   a What gas are they using up?

....

   b What gas are they producing?

....

   c Explain why the gas you named in **b** does not collect in the tube.

....

....

Exam-style questions

1 State the lowest and the highest temperature at which you would test the respiration rate in small organisms. Give reasons for your choices. **(2)**

....

....

2 The table shows the results of one experiment to measure the effect of temperature on the respiration rate of waxworms.

Temperature (°C)	Distance moved by the blob in 5 min (mm)
10	9
10	9
10	10
15	12
15	15
15	13
20	17
20	20
20	18
25	25
25	25
25	28
30	10
30	33
30	38

a Explain why the measurements were repeated for each temperature. **(1)**

....

....

b Plot all the results on a scatter diagram. **(2)**

c Identify the anomalous result. **(1)**

....

d Suggest an explanation for this anomalous result. **(1)**

....

e Draw a line of best fit through the remaining points. **(1)**

f Describe the correlation shown in your diagram. **(1)**

....

g Suggest an explanation for this correlation. **(2)**

....

....

A transect is used to study the distribution of organisms and how it is affected by changes in environmental conditions. With a belt transect, quadrats are placed at regular intervals along the transect line to sample the organisms.

Your teacher may watch to see if you can:

- work efficiently
- follow safety guidance.

Method

A   If your teacher has not told you where to place the transect, look for somewhere that shows obvious variation in environmental conditions, such as from bright light to deep shade under a tree, or from an area that shows heavy trampling to an area with less.

B   Decide which environmental factors you will measure and how you will measure them.

C   Peg out the tape measure along the ground to form the transect line.

D   Take measurements at regular intervals along the transect line (as shown in the diagram). Decide on your measurement intervals, which may depend on how long the line is and how much time you have to record information.

E   Place the top left-hand corner of the quadrat at a measurement point on the transect line.

F   Measure the environmental factors at that point and record them. Collect any soil samples using a trowel and place them in a sealed bag. Label the bag clearly to identify its position along the transect.

G   Record the abundance of your selected organisms in the quadrat.

H   Repeat steps **F–G** at each measurement point along the transect.

I   In the lab, carry out suitable tests on any soil samples and record the results.

Aim

To investigate the distribution of a species using a transect and quadrats.

Apparatus

- long tape measure (at least 20 m) with pegs at each end
- quadrat (e.g. 50 cm × 50 cm square)
- apparatus for measuring suitable abiotic factors, e.g. light sensor and recorder, soil humidity sensor, small bags for collecting soil samples for nutrient testing in the lab, trowel, anemometer (wind speed measurer)
- optional: identification charts, labels for bags and pencil

Safety ⚠

Follow any safety guidance related to the working area.

Consider the safety aspects of your chosen site, such as poisonous plants, animal faeces or open water, and take appropriate precautions while working.

Wash your hands after the experiment.

Recording your results

1 In the space below, draw a table to record the abundance of the organisms you sampled at each point along the transect line, as well as the environmental factor measurements at each point.

2 Display your results in a suitable chart or graph.

Considering your results/conclusions

3 Describe the change in distribution of your chosen organism along the transect.

....

....

....

4 Describe the change in your chosen environmental factor along the transect.

....

....

....

5 Describe any correlation between the change in distribution of the organism and the change in environmental factor.

....

....

....

6 Suggest an explanation for any correlation that you have described in **5**.

....

....

....

Evaluation

7 Describe an experiment that you could do in the lab to test whether the environmental factor you measured affects the organism as you suggest in your answer to question **6**.

....

....

....

....

....

....

....

Exam-style questions

1 Describe how a quadrat can be used to see if there is a relationship between the abundance of a plant and light intensity. **(1)**

....

....

....

2 What are abiotic factors? **(1)**

....

3 Name two abiotic factors, other than light intensity, that could change between the open ground and close to the tree, and explain why each factor could change. **(2)**

....

....

....

....

....

....

4 Explain why the abundance of a plant species might change between the open ground and close to the tree. **(2)**

....

....

....

....

....

5 a Explain how some measurements of abiotic factors would vary if taken in the afternoon rather than in the morning. **(2)**

....

....

....

....

b Explain how these variations could affect the conclusion drawn from data taken at just one time of day. **(2)**

....

....

....

Ink is a mixture of coloured substances dissolved in a liquid solvent. You will use simple distillation to separate a sample of the solvent in some ink. Read the method and answer the planning and predicting questions, before starting your experiment.

Your teacher may watch to see if you can:

● carry out experiments safely, reducing the risks from hazards.

Method

A Set up your apparatus as shown in the diagram. Put anti-bumping granules in the bottom of the flask.

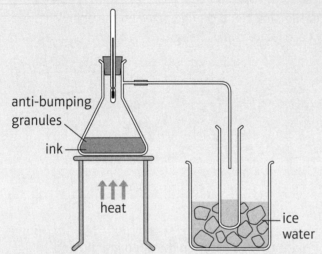

B Adjust the Bunsen burner so that you have a gentle blue flame. The air hole should be about half open and the gas tap should be about half on.

C Heat the ink until it boils.

D Collect the distillate in the test tube and note the temperature of the vapour.

Planning and predicting

1 When you distil the ink, how will you know if you have successfully purified the water?

....

....

....

2 Predict the temperature reading on the thermometer when the ink is boiling. Explain your answer.

....

....

3 What is the purpose of the ice water shown in the diagram?

....

....

Aim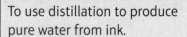

To use distillation to produce pure water from ink.

Apparatus

● eye protection
● conical flask
● delivery tube
● test tube
● ink
● Bunsen burner
● gauze
● two-hole rubber bung with thermometer
● 250 cm³ beaker
● ice
● tripod
● heat-resistant mat
● anti-bumping granules

Safety

Eye protection should be worn at all times.

Anti-bumping granules should be used to reduce the risk of the liquid boiling over.

4 The conical flask might be knocked off the tripod.

  a Why is the conical flask a hazard if knocked over?

  b How can the risk of harm from this hazard be reduced?

5 Suggest one other hazard and a way of reducing the risk from this hazard.

6 What air hole and gas settings should you have for the Bunsen burner:

  a when you are not using it

  b when you are using it to heat the ink?

Considering your results/conclusions

7 Did you purify the water successfully? Explain your answer.
Try to include a possible test you could carry out to show it was water.

8 Explain what happened when the ink was distilled. In your explanation, use the following words:
boil, evaporate, liquid, steam, temperature, vapour.

Exam-style questions

1   A student carries out simple distillation on a sample of blue ink.

    a Predict how the appearance of the ink changes, and give a reason for your answer.   **(2)**

....

....

....

....

    b During the experiment, hot liquid solvent drips from the bulb of the thermometer.
       Suggest an explanation for a temperature rise from 83 °C to 100 °C as this happens.   **(1)**

....

....

....

2   Explain why simple distillation allows a pure solvent to be separated from a solution.   **(3)**

....

....

....

....

3   A student distils a sample of ink.
    Devise a simple method to show that the liquid collected is pure water.
    Include the expected results in your answer.   **(3)**

....

....

....

....

....

....

....

....

Many inks contain a mixture of dyes. Chromatography can be used to identify inks; for example, inks from crime scenes or from documents that may have been forged.

Your teacher may watch to see if you can:

- follow instructions carefully
- draw conclusions from your results.

Method

A Check that your chromatography paper hangs close to the bottom of the empty beaker without touching it (as shown in the diagram).

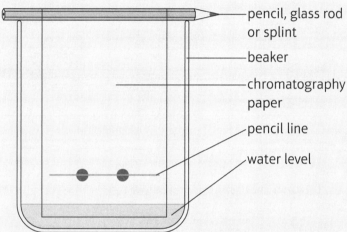

pencil, glass rod or splint

beaker

chromatography paper

pencil line

water level

B Take the paper out of the beaker and draw a pencil line on the paper, about 2 cm from the bottom.

C Put a small spot of ink from each pen on your pencil line.

D Write the name of each pen or ink below each spot with a pencil.

E Pour some water into the beaker to a depth of about 1 cm.

F Lower the chromatography paper into the beaker so that the bottom of the paper is in the water, but the water level is below the spots (see the diagram).

G Leave the paper in the beaker until the water soaks up the paper and reaches near the top of the paper. The water is the solvent for the different coloured dye compounds in each ink. The solvent is called the mobile phase in chromatography, because it is the part that it is moving.

H Take the paper out and immediately use a pencil to mark the location of the solvent front (the level the water has reached) before it evaporates. Leave it to dry.

Recording your results

1 Describe the coloured dye compounds that mixed to produce the ink in each pen.

Aim

You are going to test some inks to see how many dyes they contain and calculate their R_f values.

Apparatus

- pencil and ruler
- beaker
- chromatography paper attached to a pencil, rod or splint
- two marker pens or felt-tip pens

2 Measure the distance the solvent (the water) has risen from the pencil line.

....

3 Measure the distance that each dye spot has risen from the pencil line.
Measure from the pencil line to the top of each different coloured spot.
Write your results in the tables below.

Name of pen/ink				
Colours of dye spots				
Distance of spot from pencil line (cm)				
R_f value				

Name of pen/ink				
Colours of dye spots				
Distance of spot from pencil line (cm)				
R_f value				

Considering your results/conclusions

4 Calculate the R_f value using the formula below for each separate colour in the inks.
Add this value to your table above.

$$R_f = \frac{\text{distance moved by the coloured spot}}{\text{distance moved by solvent}}$$

5 Were any of the inks a pure colour? Explain your conclusion.

....

....

....

....

6 Did the same coloured dyes appear in more than one ink?
If so, do you think they were the same chemical compound? Explain your answer.

....

....

....

....

....

Evaluation

7 Why was the starting line drawn in pencil?

....45..

....

....

....

8 Why did you have to label the spots?

....

....

....

....

9 Why is the chromatography paper hung with the bottom just in the water?

....

....

....

....

10 Why must the water level in the beaker be below the spots?

....

....

....

....

11 How easy was it to identify the level to which each coloured dye had travelled? How would this affect the accuracy of the R_f values you calculated?

....

....

....

....

....

....

Exam-style questions

1 Propanone is a flammable solvent. A student carries out paper chromatography of ink using propanone.

   a Identify the mobile phase in her experiment. **(1)**

....

   b Identify the part of her apparatus that contained the stationary phase. **(1)**

....

   c Explain one precaution necessary to control the risk of harm in her experiment. **(1)**

....

   d Suggest an explanation for why the level of the propanone should be below the ink spot on the paper at the start. **(1)**

....

2 Explain how paper chromatography separates coloured substances in ink. **(3)**

....

....

....

....

....

....

3 A student uses paper chromatography to analyse four samples of ink (X, A, B and C). The diagram shows his results.

   a Describe what the results tell you about ink sample X. **(2)**

....

....

....

   b Calculate the R_f value of the substance in ink B. **(2)**

....

Salts, such as copper sulfate, are compounds formed by reacting an acid with a base. Copper oxide reacts with warm sulfuric acid to produce a blue solution of the salt copper sulfate. In this practical, you will use these reactants to prepare pure, dry, hydrated copper sulfate crystals.

Your teacher may watch to see if you can:
- safely and correctly use apparatus.

Method
A Pour about 20 cm³ of dilute sulfuric acid into a conical flask.

B Place the conical flask into a water bath at 50 °C and heat for 3–4 minutes to allow the acid to heat up.

C Use the spatula to add a little copper oxide to the acid and stir or swirl the contents of the flask.

D Keep repeating step **C** until the black powder does not disappear after stirring. (This makes sure the copper oxide is in excess.)

E Return the mixture to the water bath for a few minutes (to make sure there is no acid left).

F Filter the mixture into a beaker and pour into an evaporating basin.

G Place the evaporating basin on top of a beaker half full of water. Heat the beaker, evaporating basin and contents using a Bunsen burner on a blue flame.

H Heat until about half of the water has evaporated. Then allow the evaporating basin to cool.

I When cool, transfer the solution to a Petri dish or watch glass and leave for a few days to allow the water to evaporate.

J Observe the shape and colour of the copper sulfate crystals formed.

Step F

Step H

Aim
To prepare a sample of pure, dry, hydrated copper sulfate crystals starting from copper oxide.

Apparatus
- eye protection
- 100 cm³ conical flask
- 100 cm³ beaker
- Bunsen burner
- gauze and tripod
- heat mat
- Petri dish or watch glass
- 100 cm³ measuring cylinder
- evaporating basin
- spatula
- stirring rod
- filter funnel
- filter paper
- tongs
- water bath (set at 50 °C)
- dilute sulfuric acid
- copper(II) oxide

Safety ⚠
Wear eye protection at all times.

Recording your results
1 Describe the colour, shape and size of the copper sulfate crystals produced.

Dark blue, with light highlights, 3cm~0.1cm Kite/diamond shape ~~that~~ Smooth (2-D)

2 Describe the appearance of:

a the sulfuric acid

Clear Solution

b the copper oxide

Black powder

c the solution at the end of the reaction.

Light Blue Solution

Considering your results

3 Write a word equation to show the reaction you have carried out.

Sulfuric acid + Copper oxide —> Copper sulfate + water ✓

4 State why you need to be sure excess copper oxide is added in step **D**.

To make sure all the sulfuric acid is reacted
and copper oxide dissolved, high concentration

5 What would happen in step **E** if there was still some acid left?

The acid would dissolve the crystals The copper oxide
would still be dissolving

6 Name the substance left in the filter paper in step **F**.

Copper oxide

7 What is dissolved in the solution that went through the filter paper?

Copper Sulfate + water

8 Explain why this is an example of a neutralisation reaction.

acid + base ⇌ Salt + water
name

9 What substance acts as a base in this reaction?

Copper oxide

10 Write a symbol equation to show the reaction you have carried out. Include the state symbols.
Use your answer to question **3** to help you.

$H_2SO_4 + CuO(s) \longrightarrow CuSO_4 + H_2O$ (aq) (l)
state sym. (aq)

Exam-style questions

1 State why copper sulfate is described as a salt. **(1)**

Because it is a Base and acid + base = Salt + water

2 During the preparation of copper sulfate the mixture is filtered to remove copper oxide. Explain why the copper oxide gets stuck in the filter paper while the copper sulfate goes through it. **(2)**

Copper Oxide is a Solid and the bigger particles get stuck in the filter paper whereas copper Sulfate is a Solution

3 Nickel chloride ($NiCl_2$) is a soluble salt.
It can be made by reacting insoluble nickel oxide (NiO) with hydrochloric acid (HCl).

  a Write a word equation for this reaction. **(1)**

Hydrochloric acid + nickel oxide —> Nickel chloride + water

  b Write a balanced equation with state symbols. **(2)**

$$2HCl + NiO \longrightarrow NiCl_2 + H_2O$$

  c Briefly describe the three main stages involved in preparing a pure, solid sample of nickel chloride. You can draw diagrams to help with your answer. **(3)**

1.) Add excess nickel oxide to hydrochloric acid

2.) filter out excess nickel oxide

3.) Evaporate the water to leave nickel chloride

4 Two class groups prepared some zinc chloride. One group produced lots of very small crystals while the other group produced larger crystals. Suggest an explanation for the groups producing different-sized crystals. **(2)**

Stomach acid contains hydrochloric acid. Acid indigestion causes a burning feeling in the chest and throat. Antacids, which may contain magnesium hydroxide, are used to neutralise stomach acid to relieve indigestion. In this practical, you will use calcium hydroxide, which has similar properties to magnesium hydroxide, to investigate neutralisation.

Your teacher may watch to see if you can:

- carry out an experiment appropriately
- use apparatus accurately and safely.

Method

A   Use the measuring cylinder to add 50 cm³ of dilute hydrochloric acid to the beaker.

B   Estimate and record the pH of the contents of the beaker:

- Put a piece of universal indicator paper onto the white tile.
- Dip the end of the glass rod into the liquid, then tap it onto the universal indicator paper.
- Wait 30 seconds, then match the colour to the appropriate pH on the pH colour chart.
- Rinse the glass rod with water.

C   Measure out 0.3 g of calcium hydroxide powder onto a piece of paper or a 'weighing boat'.

D   Add the calcium hydroxide powder to the beaker, stir, then estimate and record the pH of the mixture.

E   Repeat step **D** seven times so that you add a total of 2.4 g of calcium hydroxide powder to the acid.

Recording your results

1   In the space below, make a table to record the pH of the contents of the beaker. Use the columns for the mass of calcium hydroxide powder added, and the pH of the mixture. Remember to leave a row for the first pH measurement (before you have added any calcium hydroxide).

Aim

Powdered calcium hydroxide reacts with hydrochloric acid. Calcium chloride solution and water are produced:

$$Ca(OH)_2(s) + 2HCl(aq) \rightarrow CaCl_2(aq) + 2H_2O(l)$$

You will investigate what happens to the pH of a fixed volume of dilute hydrochloric acid when you add calcium hydroxide to it.

Apparatus

- eye protection
- 100 cm³ beaker
- 50 cm³ measuring cylinder
- ±0.1 g balance
- spatula
- stirring rod
- white tile
- universal indicator paper
- pH colour chart
- dilute hydrochloric acid
- calcium hydroxide powder
- graph paper

Safety ⚠️

Wear eye protection. Calcium hydroxide is an irritant with a risk of serious damage to eyes. Dilute hydrochloric acid is an irritant.

Considering your results

2 Plot a line graph to show pH on the vertical axis and mass of calcium hydroxide added on the horizontal axis. Draw a curve of best fit.

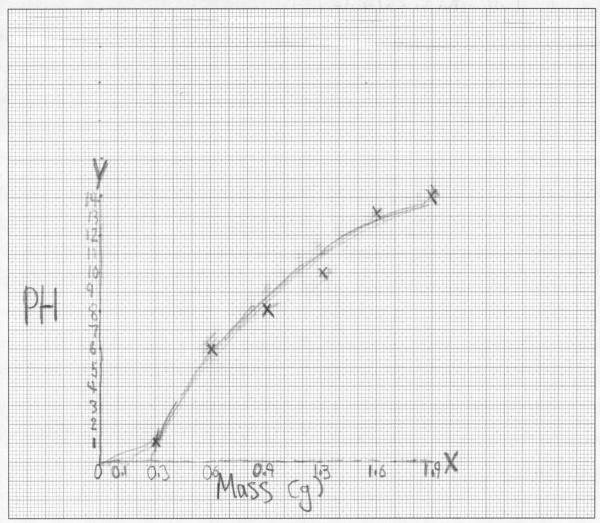

3 Describe what happens to the pH of the reaction mixture as calcium hydroxide continues to be added.

It goes up, as the Solution goes from an acid to an Alkali

4 Use your graph to determine the mass of calcium hydroxide that must be added to reach pH 7.

0.7

Evaluation

5 Explain one way to improve the accuracy of the experiment.

Repeat the experiment

Exam-style questions

1 **a** Name the soluble salt formed when hydrochloric acid reacts with calcium hydroxide. **(1)**

Calcium chloride

b Write the balanced equation, including state symbols, for the reaction between calcium hydroxide powder and dilute hydrochloric acid. **(3)**

$$Ca(OH)_{2(aq)} + 2HCl_{(aq)} \longrightarrow CaCl_2^{(aq)} + 2H_2O_{(L)}$$

2 Give *two* reasons that explain why eye protection must be worn when using dilute hydrochloric acid. **(2)**

If acid goes into the eye it can blind you

Irritant

Protection

3 A student investigates the change in pH when calcium hydroxide powder is added to $100\,cm^3$ of dilute hydrochloric acid.

a State *two* control variables in his experiment. **(2)**

Volume of acid

Concentration

b State the independent variable in his experiment. **(1)**

PH

c Describe how the student could modify his experiment to investigate temperature changes instead of pH changes. **(1)**

Use a thermometer instead of glass rod or indicator paper

4 The pH of a solution may be determined using universal indicator paper or using a pH meter.

a State why a pH meter must be calibrated using a solution with a known pH value. **(1)**

more accurate PH reve value

b Explain whether indicator paper or a pH meter has the higher resolution. **(2)**

indicator paper gives PH in whole numbers whereas PH meter can give up to 2 decimal place

The copper produced for making copper wires must be very pure. It is produced by electrolysis of copper sulfate solution.

Your teacher may watch to see if you can:
- carefully control variables during investigations
- make accurate measurements.

Method 1 – Using copper electrodes

A Select two pieces of copper foil to use as electrodes and clean them with emery paper. Label one of the electrodes as 'anode' and the other as 'cathode'.

B Measure and record the mass of each electrode.

C Half fill the beaker with copper sulfate solution.

D Set up the circuit as shown in the diagram.

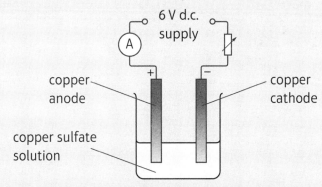

A circuit diagram for the electrolysis of copper sulfate solution using copper electrodes

E Turn the power on and adjust the variable resistor to give a current of 0.2 A. Record the current. Leave the power on for 20 minutes, adjusting the variable resistor to keep the current constant, if necessary.

F Then turn off the power and remove the electrodes from the beaker.

G Gently rinse the electrodes with distilled water and then dip them into propanone. Remove the electrodes from the propanone and gently shake them until the propanone evaporates.

H Measure and record the masses of the dry electrodes.

I Repeat the experiment using currents of 0.3 A, 0.4 A and 0.5 A.

Aim
To electrolyse copper sulfate solution using inert (graphite) electrodes and copper electrodes.

Apparatus
- eye protection
- emery paper
- low voltage d.c. supply
- ammeter
- variable resistor
- connecting leads
- crocodile clips
- $100 \, cm^3$ beaker
- stop clock
- two graphite rods
- two pieces of copper foil
- copper sulfate solution
- access to propanone (in a fume cupboard)
- access to a balance

Safety ⚠
Wear eye protection.

Propanone is an irritant. It is highly flammable; there must not be any naked flames in the laboratory.

Method 1 – Recording your results

1 Record your results in the table below, including the change in mass of each electrode.

Current (A)	Mass of anode at start (g)	Mass of anode at end (g)	Change in mass of anode (g)	Mass of cathode at start (g)	Mass of cathode at end (g)	Change in mass of cathode (g)
0.2	2.77	2.69	−0.08	2.51	2.58	0.07
0.3	2.68	2.55	−0.13	2.55	2.66	0.11
0.4	2.53	2.36	−0.017	2.62	2.76	0.14
0.5	2.335	2.15	−0.21	2.70	2.87	0.17

Method 1 – Considering your results/conclusions

2 Plot a scatter diagram of change in mass of the anode against the current. Draw a line of best fit through the points. Plot a second diagram on the same axes showing the change in mass of the cathode against the current. Again, draw a line of best fit through these points.

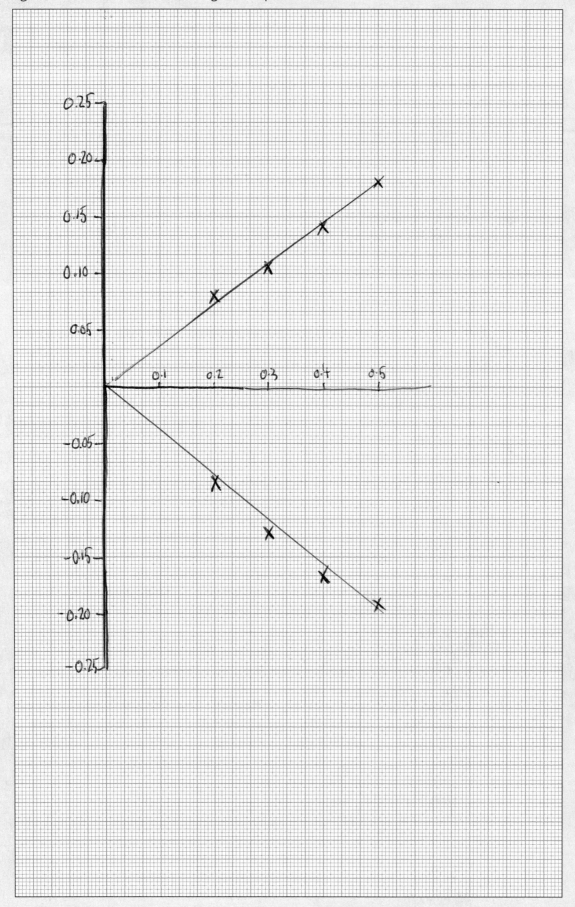

3 Describe the relationship between the change in mass at each electrode and the current.

Anode graph - the increase in mass is directly proportional

4 Explain the changes in mass of each electrode.

5 Use the diagram to predict the change in mass of the anode when the current is 0.35 A.

6 Suggest a reason why the change in mass at the cathode is not the same as the change in mass at the anode when the same current is used.

7 Describe how you could improve the experiment to be more certain that the data collected is correct and free from error.

Method 2 – Using inert electrodes

A The diagram on the right shows the circuit used for the electrolysis of copper sulfate solution with graphite electrodes. Set up the circuit as shown.

B Turn the power on.

C Observe what happens at each electrode.

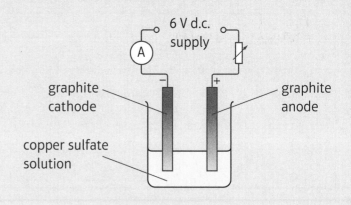

6 V d.c. supply

graphite cathode

graphite anode

copper sulfate solution

Method 2 – Recording your results

8 Record your observations and the name of the product formed at each electrode.

Method 2 – Considering your results/conclusions

9 Explain the formation of the product at each electrode.

Write a **half equation** for the formation of the product at each electrode and classify each reaction as **oxidation** or **reduction**.

node - $Cu^{2+} + 2e^- \rightarrow Cu$

de - $O^{2-} \rightarrow O^2 + 4e^-$

Exam-style questions

1   Explain why a different product is formed at the anode when copper sulfate solution is electrolysed using graphite electrodes rather than copper electrodes. **(4)**

....

....

....

....

....

....

....

2   Look at the method for electrolysis using copper electrodes.

   a   State and explain one safety precaution. **(1)**

....

....

....

....

   b   State why it is important to use clean copper electrodes. **(1)**

....

....

   c   Give a reason why a variable resistor is used in the electrolysis circuit. **(1)**

....

....

   d   Suggest a reason why the electrodes are washed at the end of the electrolysis. **(1)**

....

....

....

   e   Suggest a reason why propanone is used after washing the electrodes with distilled water. **(1)**

....

....

....

....

In this practical you will carry out an acid–alkali titration to determine the exact volume of acid that is needed to neutralise a given volume of alkali.

Your teacher may watch to see if you can:

- follow instructions
- make accurate measurements.

Method

A Place a funnel in the top of the burette then rinse and fill the burette with the dilute hydrochloric acid.

B Fill the jet below the tap by running some acid out of the burette, then remove the funnel from the top of the burette. Record the initial reading on the burette.

C Following instructions from your teacher, use the pipette filler to rinse and fill the pipette to the 25 cm^3 mark with the sodium hydroxide solution.

D Empty the sodium hydroxide solution from the pipette into a conical flask.

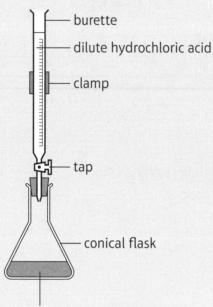

— burette
— dilute hydrochloric acid
— clamp
— tap
— conical flask

sodium hydroxide solution + methyl orange indicator

E Add a few drops of methyl orange to the conical flask, until the solution is yellow, then place the flask on a white tile under the burette.

F Add the hydrochloric acid to the sodium hydroxide solution in small portions while swirling the conical flask.

G Stop adding the hydrochloric acid when the indicator turns a peach/orange colour. Record the burette reading. This is the rough titration to give you an approximate volume of hydrochloric acid needed. If the indicator turns pink, you have added too much hydrochloric acid.

H Repeat steps **A–E** (except for rinsing the burette and pipette). Add hydrochloric acid to the sodium hydroxide until you have used 1 cm^3 less than in the rough titration. Use a wash bottle of distilled/deionised water to rinse the tip of the burette with a little water to make sure no hydrochloric acid is left there. Then add hydrochloric acid drop by drop until the solution in the flask is peach/orange. Record the burette reading.

I Repeat step **H** until you have two concordant results within 0.2 cm^3 of each other.

To prepare crystals of sodium chloride

1 Repeat the titration using 25 cm^3 of sodium hydroxide solution and the mean volume of hydrochloric acid, but do not add any indicator.

2 Pour the sodium chloride solution into an evaporating basin and heat it until crystals start to form. Take care – it starts to spit hot salt if it boils completely dry.

3 Leave the basin until it is cool and the rest of the water has evaporated. You will be left with pure, dry crystals of sodium chloride.

Aim

To find the volume of hydrochloric acid needed to neutralise 25.0 cm^3 of 0.10 mol dm^{-3} sodium hydroxide solution.

Apparatus

- eye protection
- burette and stand
- funnel
- pipette and filler
- conical flask
- white tile
- wash bottle of distilled or deionised water
- methyl orange indicator
- 0.10 mol dm^{-3} sodium hydroxide solution
- hydrochloric acid of unknown concentration

Optional:

- Bunsen burner, heat-resistant mat, tripod, gauze, tongs, evaporating basin

Safety ⚠

Eye protection must be worn. Use a pipette filler. If you heat the solution to prepare sodium chloride crystals: take care when heating the solution, because hot salt may spit out of the basin; stop heating once crystals start to form; do not touch the hot tripod and gauze.

Results

1 Record your results in the table below.

Burette reading	Titration 1	Titration 2	Titration 3	Titration 4	Titration 5
Final reading (cm³)					
Initial reading (cm³)					
Volume added (cm³)					

Conclusion

2 Calculate the mean of the concordant results (results that are within 0.2 cm³ of each other).

3 Calculate the number of moles of sodium hydroxide in 25.0 cm³ of 0.10 mol dm⁻³ sodium hydroxide solution. Use the formula:

number of moles of solute = volume of solution (dm³) × concentration (mol dm⁻³)

Remember to convert the volume in cm³ to dm³ by dividing by 1000.

4 The equation for the reaction between hydrochloric acid and sodium hydroxide is:

$$HCl + NaOH \rightarrow NaCl + H_2O$$

Work out the number of moles of hydrochloric acid that reacted with the number of moles of sodium hydroxide you calculated in question **3**.

5 Use the formula in question **3**, the mean volume of hydrochloric acid and your answer to question **4** to calculate the concentration of hydrochloric acid in mol dm⁻³. Remember to convert the volume in cm³ to dm³.

Exam-style questions

1 Give a reason why the burette and pipette should be rinsed before they are filled. **(1)**

....

2 Give a reason for standing the conical flask on a white tile. **(1)**

....

3 State what is meant by the 'end point' of the titration. **(1)**

....

4 $25 \, cm^3$ of sodium hydroxide solution was titrated with dilute hydrochloric acid:

$HCl + NaOH \rightarrow NaCl + H_2O$

The following results were obtained.

	Titration 1	**Titration 2**	**Titration 3**
final burette reading (cm^3)	26.00	26.30	27.20
initial burette reading (cm^3)	0.00	1.20	1.90
volume of acid used (cm^3)	26.00	25.10	

    a Calculate the volume of acid used in titration 3. **(1)**

....

    b Calculate the volume of acid that should be used to react with $25 \, cm^3$ of the sodium hydroxide solution to produce the salt sodium chloride. Give a reason for your answer. **(2)**

....

    c Describe how you would use the volume calculated in **b** to obtain pure, dry crystals of sodium chloride. **(3)**

....

....

H   **d** The sodium hydroxide solution had a concentration of $0.100 \, mol \, dm^{-3}$. Calculate the concentration, in $mol \, dm^{-3}$, of the hydrochloric acid used in this experiment. **(3)**

....

The progress of a chemical reaction can be measured by how the amounts of reactant or product change with time.

Your teacher may watch to see if you can:

- carefully control variables during investigations
- measure change accurately.

Method

Task 1

A Set up the apparatus as shown in the diagram.

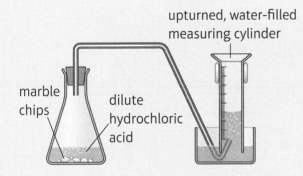

upturned, water-filled measuring cylinder

marble chips

dilute hydrochloric acid

B Measure 40 cm³ of 4 g dm⁻³ hydrochloric acid into a conical flask.

C Add 5 g of small marble chips to the flask.

D Immediately stopper the flask and start the stop clock/watch.

E Note the total volume of gas produced after every 30 seconds for five minutes or until the reaction has finished.

F Repeat steps **A–E** using 5 g of larger marble chips.

Task 2

G Follow steps **A–D** above.

H Note the amount of carbon dioxide produced in one minute.

I Repeat steps **G** and **H** using 3.2, 2.4, 1.6 and 0.8 g dm⁻³ acid.

Aim

To investigate the effect on the rate of reaction of changing the surface area of solids and the concentration of solutions, by measuring the production of a gas.

Apparatus

- eye protection
- balance
- water trough
- 100 cm³ measuring cylinder
- stop clock
- conical flask
- delivery tube and bung
- marble chips (small)
- marble chips (large)
- dilute hydrochloric acid (4 g dm⁻³)

Safety ⚠

Wear eye protection at all times. Care is needed with acid solutions. Wash off splashes immediately.

Recording your results

Task 1

Record your results in the table below.

Time (min)	0	0.5	1.0	1.5	2.0	2.5	3.0	3.5	4.0	4.5	5.0
Small chips – volume of gas (cm³)	0	60	155	230	255						
Large chips – volume of gas (cm³)	0	12	52	90	130	160	184	195	220	235	250

Task 2

Record your results in the table below.

Concentration of acid (g dm⁻³)	0.8	1.6	2.4	3.2	4.0
Volume of gas produced in one minute (cm³)	5	50	75	125	180

Considering your results/conclusion

Task 1

1 Use your results to draw a scatter diagram of volume of gas against time for small chips and the same scatter diagram for large chips on the same axes. Put time on the horizontal axis and volume of gas on the vertical axis. Draw a line of best fit for each scatter diagram, using different-coloured lines and labels.

2 Explain how you can tell from the scatter diagrams when the reactions were finished.

3 Describe how the size of the marble chips is related to the surface area for a fixed mass of chips.

4 Describe how increasing the surface area affects the rate of reaction.

5 Explain how your results and scatter diagrams fit with your conclusion in question **4**.

Task 2

6 Use your results to draw a scatter diagram of concentration of acid against volume of gas produced in one minute. Put volume of gas on the horizontal axis and concentration on the vertical axis.

7 Describe how the rate of the reaction is related to the concentration of the acid.

....

....

....

8 Explain how your results and diagram fit with your conclusion in question **7**.

....

....

....

Evaluation

Task 1

9 Suggest possible sources of error in this investigation.

....
....
....
....

10 Suggest possible changes to the method that could improve the reliability of the results.

....
....
....
....
....

Task 2

11 Suggest possible sources of error in this investigation.

....
....
....
....
....
....
....

12 Suggest possible changes to the method that could improve the reliability of the results.

....
....
....
....
....
....

Exam-style questions

1 When copper carbonate reacts with sulfuric acid, carbon dioxide gas is formed.
Explain how an electronic balance could be used to investigate the rate of this reaction. **(3)**

....

....

....

....

....

....

....

2 Look at the graph.

a State when the reaction is complete. Explain your answer. **(2)**

....

....

....

....

....

....

....

b Sketch the graph and add a curve that would be produced by smaller marble chips. **(2)**

c Use the graph at the start of the question to calculate the average reaction rate in cm^3/min between 45 and 105 seconds. Show your working. **(2)**

....

d Describe how you would use a tangent line to estimate the reaction rate in cm^3/min at 100 seconds. **(3)**

....

....

....

....

....

....

....

....

....

The progress of a chemical reaction can be measured by how long a reaction takes to reach a certain point.

Your teacher may watch to see if you can:

- carefully control variables during investigations
- measure change accurately
- work safely.

Method

A Decide on four temperatures between 20 °C and 50 °C, which you are going to investigate.

B Place 10 cm³ of sodium thiosulfate solution and 40 cm³ of water into a 250 cm³ conical flask.

C Measure 5 cm³ of dilute hydrochloric acid into a test tube.

D Clamp the conical flask in place in a water bath at your first chosen temperature. Place the test tube in a rack in the same water bath.

E Record your chosen temperature.

F After five minutes, remove the flask and place it on a piece of white paper marked with a cross, as shown opposite.

G Add the acid to the thiosulfate and start the stop clock.

H Looking down from above, stop the clock when the cross disappears.

I Note this time and the final temperature of the mixture.

J Repeat steps **A–I** for the other chosen temperatures.

Recording your results

1 Draw a table in the space below with two columns: one for temperature, and the other for the time taken for the cross to disappear. Don't forget the units. Record the results of your experiments.

Aim

To investigate the effect of changing the temperature on the rate of reaction between sodium thiosulfate and hydrochloric acid, by observing a colour change in the solutions.

Apparatus

- eye protection
- 250 cm³ conical flask
- 10 cm³ measuring cylinder
- 50 cm³ measuring cylinder
- stop clock
- test tube
- test tube rack
- water bath
- white paper with cross
- sodium thiosulfate solution
- dilute hydrochloric acid

Safety ⚠

Wear eye protection at all times.

Care is needed with acid solutions. Wash off splashes immediately.

Considering your results/conclusion

2   Draw a scatter diagram of your results, with temperature on the horizontal axis. Draw a line of best fit.

3   **a** Describe how temperature affects the rate of the reaction.

....

....

....

b Explain your answer to part **a** by referring to the shape of your diagram.

....

....

....

4 If the rate of reaction doubled, what would happen to the time taken for the cross to disappear?

....

....

....

5 a What temperature rise roughly doubles the rate of the reaction?

....

....

....

b Use the values from your scatter diagram to explain your answer to part **a**.

....

....

....

....

Evaluation

6 Describe two possible sources of error in this investigation.

....

....

....

....

....

....

7 Suggest a way of reducing one of these errors.

....

....

....

....

....

....

Exam-style questions

1 Explain why acid reacts faster with powdered chalk than with lumps of chalk. **(3)**

....

....

....

2 Some results from a 'disappearing cross' experiment are shown in the table.

Mean temperature (°C)	Time taken for cross to disappear (s)
20	165
30	81
40	42
50	21

a State why the cross disappears. **(1)**

....

....

b Sketch a graph of the results with temperature on the horizontal axis. **(3)**

c Explain what these results tell us about the effect of temperature on the rate of this reaction. **(2)**

....

....

d Describe one way of improving the results obtained from this investigation. **(1)**

....

....

In this practical you will burn alcohols in spirit burners and heat water in a beaker or copper can. You can heat the water for a given amount of time and measure the temperature rise of the water and the mass of alcohol that was burned.

Your teacher may watch to see if you can:

● keep careful control of control variables.

Method

A Measure the mass of an alcohol burner and cap. Record the mass and the name of the alcohol.

B Place the alcohol burner in the centre of a heat-resistant mat.

C Use a measuring cylinder to add 100 cm³ of cold water to a conical flask.

D Measure and record the initial temperature of the water and carefully clamp the flask above the alcohol burner.

E Surround the apparatus with a draught screen/insulation.

F Remove the cap from the burner, then light the wick of the burner and allow the water to heat up by around 40 °C.

G Replace the cap on the burner and measure and record the final temperature of the water.

H Measure the mass of the alcohol burner and cap again and record the mass.

I Wash out the flask with cold water and repeat steps **A–H** using fresh cold water and a different alcohol.

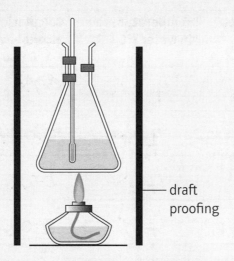

draft proofing

Aim

To investigate the temperature rise produced in a known mass of water by the combustion of the alcohols ethanol, propanol, butanol and pentanol.

Apparatus

● 100 cm³ measuring cylinder
● 250 cm³ conical flask
● stand boss head and clamp
● heat-resistant mat
● eye protection
● thermometer
● insulation/draught shield
● electronic balance
● spirit burners with caps containing: ethanol, propanol, butanol and pentanol

Safety ⚠

Wear eye protection at all times.

All alcohols are flammable: handle with care and keep the tops on burners when not in use.

Recording your results

1 Record all your measurements in the table below.

Alcohol	Mass of burner + lid at start (g)	Mass of burner + lid at end (g)	Temperature of water at start (°C)	Temperature of water at end (°C)
ethanol				
propanol				
butanol				
pentanol				

Considering your results/conclusions

2 For each alcohol:

a Calculate the change in mass of the burner and lid. Fill in your answers in the table below.

b Calculate the change in temperature of the water. Fill in your answers in the table below.

c Divide the mass of each alcohol burnt by the change in temperature. This gives you the mass of each alcohol burnt to produce for a 1 °C rise in temperature. Fill in your answers in the table below.

Alcohol	Mass of alcohol burnt (g)	Temperature rise in water (°C)	Calculation of mass of alcohol needed to produce a 1 °C rise in temperature.
ethanol	1.93	40 °C	0.03 0.04825
propanol	1.38	40 °C	0.0345
butanol	1.21	40 °C	0.03
pentanol	0.9	40 °C	0.0225

3 a Describe any trends that you can see in your results.

....

....

....

b Explain why these alcohols show such a regular trend in these values. (*Hint:* think about molecular structures.)

....

....

....

....

....

Evaluation

4 State four possible sources of error in this experiment and explain which is the main source of error.

....

....

....

....

Exam-style questions

1   Look at the investigation apparatus set up in the diagram below.

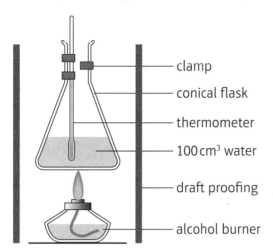

- clamp
- conical flask
- thermometer
- 100 cm³ water
- draft proofing
- alcohol burner

a Describe how the position of the flask and the alcohol burner will need to be controlled during each repeat.   (1)

The flisk must be placed the same distance from the flame

b Explain the purpose of the draught screen/insulation.   (1)

to prevent heat loss

c Describe another safety precaution that will need to be taken, in addition to wearing eye protection.   (1)

Do not pour alcohol near flame

2   In another experiment, 1.5 g of butanol produces a temperature rise of 50 °C in 100 cm³ of water. Calculate the mass of butanol that needs to be burned to cause a 1 °C rise in the same volume of water.   (1)

0.03g

Flame tests are used to identify metal **cations** in substances. Different ions produce different colours when put into a hot flame. For example, copper ions produce a blue-green flame test colour.

Your teacher may watch to see if you can:

- carry out an experiment appropriately
- use apparatus accurately and safely.

Cleaning the flame test loop

A Light the Bunsen burner and open the air hole to give a hot blue flame.

B Dip the flame test loop into the dilute hydrochloric acid. Hold the loop in the flame, then dip it in a beaker of water.

C If you see an intense flame colour in step **B**, repeat step **B** until you only see a faint flame colour or none.

Determining flame test colours

D Dip the clean flame test loop into one of the four known solids (containing Li^+, Na^+, K^+ or Ca^{2+} ions).

E Hold the loop in the edge of a hot blue flame, as shown in the diagram. Observe and record the flame test colour produced in the table below.

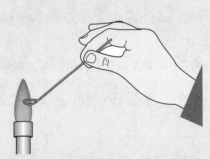

F Test the other known solids, as in steps **D** and **E**, remembering to clean the loop before each test.

Identifying metal ions

G Carry out flame tests on the four unknown solids. Observe and record each flame test colour.

Recording your results

Record the flame test colours of the known and unknown solids in the tables below.

Metal ion	Flame test colour
lithium, Li^+	
sodium, Na^+	
potassium, K^+	
calcium, Ca^{2+}	

Unknown	Flame test colour
1	
2	
3	
4	

Considering your results/conclusions

1 Use the flame test colours to identify the metal ions in each unknown solid. Complete the table.

Unknown	Metal ion
1	
2	
3	
4	

Aim

You will determine the flame test colours for lithium, sodium, potassium and calcium ions. You will then use flame tests to identify the metal ions in different unknown solids.

Apparatus

- eye protection
- Bunsen burner
- heat-resistant mat
- flame test loop
- beaker
- dilute hydrochloric acid
- test tubes
- test tube rack
- known solids
- unknown solids

Safety ⚠️

Wear eye protection.

Hydrochloric acid and test solutions are irritants.

Substances on the flame test loop may spit when in the Bunsen burner flame. Close the air hole in between tests to give a luminous flame.

Evaluation

2   Explain why you need to clean the flame test loop in between each flame test.

> remove residual substances that could affect results in future tests.

3   Explain whether it was difficult to identify the metal ions in any of the unknown solids.

> faint flame colour so difficult to distinguish flame colour, some substance dropped into Bunsen which obscured the flame colour of testing substance

Exam-style questions

1   Match the ions and the colours that they give in the flame test.   (5)

Li⁺	●
Na⁺	●
K⁺	●
Ca²⁺	●
Cu²⁺	●

●	orange-red
●	red
●	blue-green
●	yellow
●	lilac

2   A teacher demonstrates how to carry out flame tests using a platinum wire loop.

  a Give *two* reasons that explain why platinum is a suitable metal to use.   (2)

  b Give a reason that explains why a luminous Bunsen burner flame is *not* suitable for flame tests.   (1)

  c The teacher uses hydrochloric acid to clean the wire loop between each test. Explain why the teacher cleans the wire loop.   (2)

Dilute sodium hydroxide solution is used to identify metal ions in solution. It forms different coloured **precipitates** with certain dissolved metal compounds.

Your teacher may watch to see if you can:

- carry out an experiment appropriately
- use apparatus accurately and safely.

Determining metal hydroxide precipitate colours

A   Using a dropping pipette, fill a test tube to a depth of about 2 cm with one of the five known solutions (containing Al^{3+}, Ca^{2+}, Cu^{2+}, Fe^{2+} or Fe^{3+} ions).

B   Using a different dropping pipette, add a few drops of sodium hydroxide solution to the tube. Hold the test tube near the top and shake the bottom gently from side to side to mix its contents.

C   Observe and record the colour of the precipitate produced.

D   If a white precipitate forms in step **C**, add more sodium hydroxide solution until the test tube is about half full. Observe and record whether the precipitate disappears to leave a colourless solution.

E   Repeat steps **A–D** with the other known solutions. Do not contaminate one solution with another.

Identifying metal ions

F   Carry out steps **A–D** on the five unknown solutions. Observe and record the colour of each precipitate and whether any white precipitate formed disappears when excess sodium hydroxide solution is added.

Recording your results

1   Record the precipitate colours of the known and unknown solutions in the tables below.

Metal ion	Precipitate colour	Effect of adding excess sodium hydroxide
aluminium, Al^{3+}	White	clear
calcium, Ca^{2+}	White	Stayed white
copper, Cu^{2+}	blue	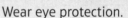
iron(II), Fe^{2+}	Green	yellow
iron(III), Fe^{3+}	orange/red	

Unknown	Precipitate colour
1	
2	
3	
4	
5	

Aim

Dilute sodium hydroxide solution is used to identify metal ions in solution. It forms different coloured **precipitates** with certain dissolved metal compounds.

You will find out the metal hydroxide precipitate colours for aluminium, calcium, copper, iron(II) and iron(III) ions. You will then use these tests to identify the metal ions in different unknown solutions.

Apparatus

- eye protection
- dropping pipettes
- test tubes
- test tube rack
- dilute sodium hydroxide solution
- known solutions
- unknown solutions

Safety ⚠

Wear eye protection.

Sodium hydroxide solution is an irritant. Avoid skin contact.

Considering your results/conclusions

2 Use your results to identify the metal ions present in each unknown solution.
Complete the table.

Unknown	Metal ion
1	
2	
3	
4	
5	

Evaluation

3 Explain why step **D** is needed to identify some metal ions in solution.

....

....

....

....

Exam-style questions

1 Some metal cations react with sodium hydroxide solution to form metal hydroxide precipitates.

a Complete the table below. (3)

Metal cation	Colour of metal hydroxide
aluminium, Al^{3+}	white
calcium, Ca^{2+}	white
copper, Cu^{2+}	
iron(II), Fe^{2+}	
iron(III), Fe^{3+}	

b Describe a test to distinguish between aluminium hydroxide and calcium hydroxide. (2)

....

....

....

....

....

....

....

....

In this practical you will identify halide ions, sulfate ions or carbonate ions.

Your teacher may watch to see if you can:

● use apparatus accurately and safely.

Testing for halide ions

A   Fill a test tube to a depth of about 2 cm with one of the solutions containing halide ions (Cl^-, Br^- or I^- ions).

B   Add a few drops of dilute nitric acid. Hold the tube near the top and shake the bottom gently from side to side to mix its contents.

C   Add a few drops of silver nitrate solution. Record the colour of the precipitate produced.

D   Repeat steps **A–C** with the other known solutions that contain halide ions (Cl^-, Br^- or I^- ions).

Testing for sulfate ions

E   Fill a test tube to a depth of about 2 cm with the solution containing sulfate ions, SO_4^{2-}.

F   Add a few drops of dilute hydrochloric acid. Hold the tube near the top and shake the bottom gently from side to side to mix its contents.

G   Add a few drops of barium chloride solution. Record the colour of the precipitate produced.

Testing for carbonate ions

H   Fill a test tube to a depth of about 2 cm with the solution containing carbonate ions, CO_3^{2-}.

I   Add a few drops of dilute hydrochloric acid. Record whether bubbling occurs.   .

Identifying anions in solution

J   Fill a test tube to a depth of about 2 cm with one of the unknown solutions.

K   Carry out a test for halide ions or for sulfate ions. Also look for bubbling (and so the presence of carbonate ions) when you acidify the solution with dilute nitric or with dilute hydrochloric.

L   Repeat steps **J** and **K** until you have determined which anions each unknown solution contains.

Aim

You will use simple chemical tests to identify **halide ions** (Cl^-, Br^- or I^-), sulfate ions (SO_4^{2-}) or carbonate ions (CO_3^{2-}) in known solutions. You will then use these tests to identify the anions in different unknown solutions.

Apparatus

● eye protection
● dropping pipettes
● test tubes
● test tube rack
● dilute nitric acid
● silver nitrate solution
● dilute hydrochloric acid
● barium chloride solution
● known solutions
● unknown solutions

Safety ⚠

Wear eye protection and avoid skin contact with the substances used.

Barium chloride solution is harmful.

Dilute nitric acid is an irritant.

Recording your results

Record your results in the tables below:

Testing for halide ions

Halide ion	Silver halide precipitate colour
Cl^-	
Br^-	
I^-	

Unknown	Observations
1	
2	
3	
4	
5	

Testing for sulfate ions

Sulfate ion	Precipitate colour
SO_4^{2-}	

Unknown	Observations
1	
2	
3	
4	
5	

Testing for carbonate ions

Carbonate ion	Bubbling visible (yes/no)
CO_3^{2-}	

Unknown	Observations
1	
2	
3	
4	
5	

Considering your results/conclusions

1   Use your results to identify the anions in each unknown solution. Complete the table below.

Unknown	Anion
1	
2	
3	
4	
5	

Evaluation

2   Silver carbonate and barium carbonate are insoluble solids. Suggest an explanation for why dilute acids are added to the test solutions in steps **B** and **F**.

Exam-style questions

1 Halide ions can be identified using silver nitrate solution.
Complete the table below. Place a tick (✓) in one box of each row to show the colour of the silver halide precipitate formed. **(3)**

Halide ion	Colour of silver halide		
	white	**yellow**	**cream**
chloride, Cl⁻			
bromide, Br⁻			
iodide, I⁻			

2 Describe the laboratory test for carbon dioxide. **(2)**

....

....

....

....

3 A student tests a solution of an unknown salt. He adds a few drops of dilute nitric acid followed by a few drops of silver nitrate solution.

   a Give a reason that explains why he adds dilute nitric acid. **(1)**

....

....

....

....

   b Explain why he should *not* use dilute hydrochloric acid instead of dilute nitric acid. **(2)**

....

....

....

....

....

....

....

In drag racing, the aim is to get to the end of a straight track as quickly as possible. The most important feature of the bike is its acceleration. Drag racers try to improve the performance of their bikes by changing the force produced by the engine and the tyres or by changing the mass of the bike. In this practical, you are going to use trolleys as a model of a motorbike to investigate the effects that mass and force have on acceleration.

Your teacher may watch to see if you can:

- follow instructions safely
- take careful measurements.

Method

A Prop up one end of the ramp and place a trolley on it. Adjust the slope of the ramp until the trolley just starts to move on its own. Gravity pulling the trolley down the slope is now slightly greater than the friction in the trolley's wheels.

B Stick a piece of card to the top of the trolley using sticky putty. Leave enough space to stack some masses on top of the trolley. Measure the length of the card and write it down.

C Find the mass of the trolley and write it down.

D Fasten the pulley at the bottom end of the ramp, and arrange the string and masses as shown below.

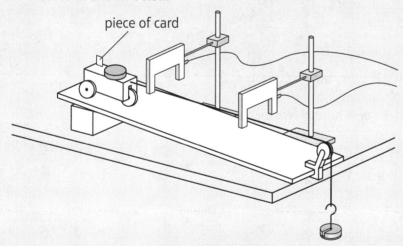

piece of card

E Set up two light gates, one near the top of the ramp and one near the bottom.
Adjust their positions so that the card on the top of the trolley passes through each gate as it runs down the ramp.

F Put a mass on the end of the string. You will keep this mass the same for all your tests. You will have to decide what mass to use.

G Release the trolley from the top of the ramp and write down the speed of the trolley (from the datalogger) as it passes through *each* light gate. Also write down the time it takes for the trolley to go from one light gate to the other.

H Repeat step **G** for other masses on the trolley. You will have to decide what masses to use, how many different masses you are going to test, and whether you need to repeat any of your tests.

Aim

To investigate the effect of mass on the acceleration of a trolley.

Apparatus

- trolley
- ramp
- blocks to prop up the end of the ramp
- string
- pulley
- masses
- sticky tape
- card
- sticky putty
- balance
- two light gates
- datalogger
- two clamps and stands
- box of crumpled newspaper

Safety ⚠

Make sure masses cannot fall on your feet by placing a box of crumpled newspaper on the floor beneath them.

Prediction

1 You will accelerate a trolley using a constant force. What effect do you think the mass of the trolley will have on the acceleration? Explain your prediction if you can. Record your prediction and ideas in the box below.

....

....

Recording your results

2 Record your results in the table below.

Mass added to trolley (kg)	Total mass of trolley and masses (kg)	Run number	u – 1st velocity reading (m/s)	v – 2nd velocity reading (m/s)	Time between velocity measurements (s)	Acceleration (m/s²)
		1				
		2				
		3				
		Mean				

3 Calculate the acceleration for each run using the formula in the box.

4 Find the mean acceleration for each trolley mass.

$$\text{acceleration} = \frac{\text{change in velocity}}{\text{time}}$$
$$a = \frac{(v - u)}{t}$$

Considering your results

5 Plot a scatter diagram to show your results. Put the total mass of the trolley on the horizontal axis and the acceleration on the vertical axis, as shown in the diagram. Draw a line or curve of best fit through your points.

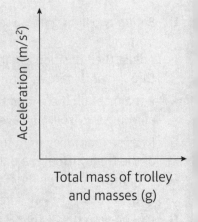

Acceleration (m/s²)

Total mass of trolley and masses (g)

6 a What relationship between acceleration and mass does your graph show?

....

....

....

b Is this what you predicted?

....

....

....

Evaluation

7 a How close are the points on your graph to the line of best fit?

....

....

....

b What does this tell you about the quality of the data you have gathered?

....

....

....

8 How do your results compare to the results obtained by other groups?

....

....

....

....

9 How certain are you that your conclusion is correct? Explain your answer.

....

....

....

Exam-style questions

1 The light gates and datalogger record the speed of the trolley at the top of the ramp and at the bottom of the ramp, and also record the time the trolley takes to move between the two light gates. Describe how this information can be used to calculate the acceleration. **(2)**

....

....

....

....

2 Use the results shown in this graph to draw a conclusion for this part of the investigation. **(1)**

....

....

....

....

....

....

....

3 Look at this graph.

a Use this graph to draw a conclusion for this part of the investigation. **(1)**

....

....

b Explain how you would present the data in this graph to allow you to draw a better conclusion. **(2)**

....

....

....

The speed, frequency and wavelength of waves can be measured in different ways. The most suitable equipment for carrying out these measurements depends on the type of wave and on its speed.

Your teacher may watch to see if you can:

- follow instructions carefully
- make accurate measurements.

Part 1. Speed of waves on water

Method

A Set up a ripple tank with a straight dipper near one of the short sides of the tank. Fasten a ruler to one of the long sides so you can see the markings above the water level.

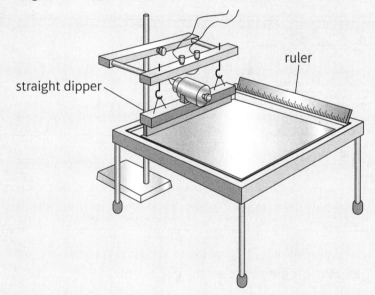

straight dipper

ruler

B Vary the current to the motor until you get waves with a wavelength about half as long as the ripple tank (so you can always see two waves).

C Count how many waves are formed in 10 seconds and write it down in the space below.

D Look at the waves against the ruler. Use the markings on the ruler to estimate the wavelength of the waves. If you have one, use a camera to take a photo of the waves with a ruler held just above them. Write your estimated wavelength down in the space below.

E Mark two points on the edge of the ripple tank and measure the distance between them. Use the stop clock to find out how long it takes a wave to go from one mark to the other. Add this value to your other pieces of data below.

Recording your results

Number of waves counted [Step **C**]:

23

Estimated wavelength [Step **D**]:

6cm

Distance between two points [Step **E**]:

92.5cm

Time taken for wave to go between two points [Step **E**]:

7secs

Aim

To measure waves in different ways and evaluate the suitability of the equipment.

Apparatus

- ripple tank
- stop clock
- ruler
- digital camera

Safety ⚠

Mop up any spilled water straight away.

Using your results

1 Calculate the speed of a single wave by dividing the distance by the time (both from step **E**). Make sure your distance is in metres and your time is in seconds.

> 0.925 ÷ 7
>
> BM   0·132

2 Find the frequency by taking the number of waves in 10 seconds (from step **C**) and dividing by 10. Then calculate the speed of the series of waves by multiplying the wavelength (from step **D**) by the frequency you have just worked out.

> 23 ÷ 10 = 2·3
>
> 2·3 Hz

Considering your results/conclusions

3 Compare your results from questions **1** and **2** with results obtained by other groups. Are your results similar? If not, can you explain the differences?

> Very similar   Slight difference in frequency

Evaluation

4 How easy was it to measure the frequency in step **C**? Why did you count the number of waves in 10 seconds?

> Because it is easier to get a more accurate answer

5 How easy was it to measure the wavelength in step **D**? It was suggested that you use a camera to help you do this. What benefit would there be in doing this?

6 How easy was it to time a single wave in step **E**? Is there any way you could improve this measurement?

Part 2. Measuring waves in a solid

Method

A Suspend a metal rod horizontally using clamp stands and rubber bands, as shown in the diagram below.

B Hit one end of the rod with a hammer. Hold a smartphone with a frequency app near the rod and note down the peak frequency.

C Measure the length of the rod and write it down. The wavelength will be twice the length of the rod.

Apparatus
● metre rule
● hammer
● two clamps and stands
● long metal rod
● rubber bands
● smartphone with frequency app

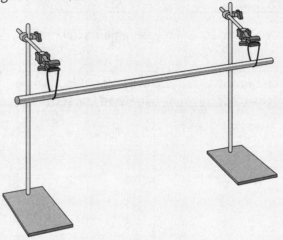

Recording your results

1 Use the frequency (from step **B**) and the wavelength (from step **C**) to calculate the speed of sound in the metal rod.

Frequency [step **B**]: 2.5 K

Wavelength [step **C**]: 122cm

Your calculation for the speed of sound in the metal rod:

Wavelength × frequency = velocity

1.22 × 2.5 =

Considering your results/conclusions

2 What is the speed of sound in the material you tested?

Evaluation

3 Explain which of your measurements is the more accurate: the wavelength or the frequency.

4 Complete the table to summarise the equipment you used for the measurements in both parts of this investigation, and how suitable the equipment was.

What was measured?	Which material was this measured for?	How was it measured?	Why was this method chosen?

5 You can measure walking speed using a tape measure and a stop clock. Explain why these instruments are not suitable for measuring the speed of sound in a solid.

Exam-style questions

1. A sound wave in air travels 660 metres in 2 seconds.
   Calculate the speed of the sound wave. (2)

2. A sound wave travelling in water has a frequency of 100 Hz.
   The speed of sound in water is 1482 m/s.
   Calculate the wavelength of the wave. (2)

3. Adanna is watching waves on the sea go past two buoys.
   She knows the buoys are 20 metres apart.
   Describe how she can find the speed of the waves. (2)

4. The speed of sound in air can be measured by finding the time it takes for a sound to echo
   from a nearby wall, and measuring the distance to the wall.

   Hitting the end of a metal rod with a hammer causes sound waves to travel along the rod.
   They reflect from the far end of the rod and continue to move up and down the rod until
   the energy dissipates. Give a reason why the method used for finding the speed of sound
   in air cannot be used for finding the speed of sound in a metal. (2)

Electromagnetic waves travel at different speeds in different materials. Light slows down when it goes from air into glass or water. If light hits the interface at an angle, it changes direction. This is called refraction. In this practical, you will investigate how the direction of a ray of light changes as it enters and leaves a glass block.

Your teacher may watch to see if you can:

- measure angles accurately.

Method

A Place a piece of plain paper on the desk. Set up the power supply, ray box and single slit so that you can shine a single ray of light across the paper on your desk.

B Place a rectangular glass block on the paper. Draw around the block.

C Shine a ray of light into your block. Use small crosses to mark where the rays of light go.

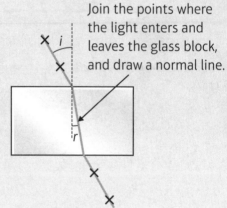

Join the points where the light enters and leaves the glass block, and draw a normal line.

D Take the block off the paper. Use a ruler to join the crosses and show the path of the light, and extend the line so it meets the outline of the block. Join the points where the light entered and left the block to show where it travelled inside the block.

E Measure the angles of incidence and refraction where the light entered the block, and measure the angles where it left the block.

F Repeat steps **C** to **E** with the ray entering the block at different angles.

G Move the ray box so that the light ray reaches the interface at right angles. Note what happens to the light as it enters and leaves the block.

Aim

To investigate how light is affected when it travels from air into glass, or from glass into air.

Apparatus

- ray box with single slit
- power supply
- rectangular glass block
- ruler
- protractor
- plain paper

Safety ⚠

Ray boxes may get hot.

Recording your results

1 Record your results in this table.

Air to glass (light entering the block)		Glass to air (light leaving the block)	
Angle i	**Angle r**	**Angle i**	**Angle r**
0°	0°	0°	0°
38°	24°	24°	38°
22°	12°	12°	22°
10°	5°	5°	10°

2 Draw a scatter diagram to show your results. Put the angle of incidence on the horizontal
axis. Plot the air-to-glass points and draw a smooth curve of best fit. Repeat for the
glass-to-air points, on the same set of axes.

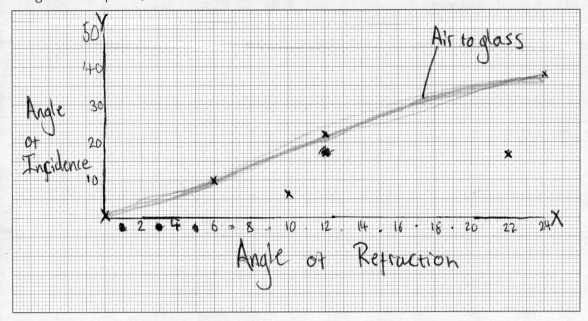

Considering your results

3 Describe the results shown by your diagram.

Air to glass $I > R$

glass to air $R > I$

4 How does the direction of the ray of light leaving the glass block compare with that of the
ray entering it?

The lines are ~~parallel~~ ~~parallel~~ ~~parallel~~ ~~parallel~~
parallel, air to glass light is bent towards the normal

5 Write a conclusion for your investigation.

Evaluation

6 **a** How accurate were your measurements?

b Is there any way you could improve your measurements?

Exam-style questions

1 Describe the difference between the way that light travels through glass compared with the way in which it travels through air. **(1)**

....

....

2 The table shows a student's results from this investigation.

Air to glass		Glass to air	
i	r	i	r
10°	6°	6°	6°
20°	13°	13°	20°
30°	20°	20°	31°
40°	25°	25°	40°
50°	30°	30°	50°
60°	34°	34°	58°
70°	38°	38°	69°
80°	40°	40°	78°

a Use the data in the table to plot a scatter diagram to show the results for light going from air to glass. Put the angle of incidence on the horizontal axis, and join your points with a smooth curve of best fit. **(5)**

b Use the table and your diagram to write a conclusion for this part of the investigation. **(3)**

....

....

....

....

....

....

c Use your graph to find the angle of refraction when the angle of incidence is 15°. **(1)**

....

....

....

....

....

....

....

....

3 If light passes through a glass block with parallel sides, the ray that comes out should be parallel with the ray that goes in. This means that the angle of incidence for air to glass should be the same as the angle of refraction from glass to air.

Look at the table in question **2**. Suggest one source of random error that may have caused the differences in these angles. **(1)**

....

....

....

....

....

Physics

SP5g
Core practical 4:
Investigating radiation

Different surfaces transfer different amounts of energy by radiation.

Your teacher may watch to see if you can:

- take careful measurements
- present your results as a line graph.

Method

A Cover four boiling tubes in different coloured materials. Try to use the same type of material (e.g. paper) for each tube, and the same thickness. Fasten the materials in place with sticky tape.

B Use the measuring cylinder to help you to pour the same volume of hot water from a kettle into each tube.

C Measure the temperature of the water in each tube and start a stop clock.

D Record the temperature of the water in each tube every two minutes for 20 minutes.

Recording your results

1 Record your results in the table below.

Time (min)	Red Temperature (°C) White	Tin	Black	
	Tube 1	Tube 2	Tube 3	Tube 4
0	80	70	72	66
2	69	58	69	54
4	65	54	66	50
6	61	50	64	45
8	58	46	61	40
10	504	43	56	
12	50	40	55	
14	48	39	53	
16	46	38	51	
18	44	37	49	
20	43	35	48	

Aim

You are going to investigate the effect of different coloured surfaces on the amount of energy transferred by radiation from a boiling tube of hot water.

Apparatus

- four boiling tubes
- test tube rack
- measuring cylinder
- four thermometers
- stop clock
- insulating materials
- sticky tape
- hot water

Safety ⚠

Take care with hot water.

2 Draw a line graph to present your results. Time should go on the horizontal axis.
Plot all four sets of results on the same axes and join each set of points with a smooth curve.

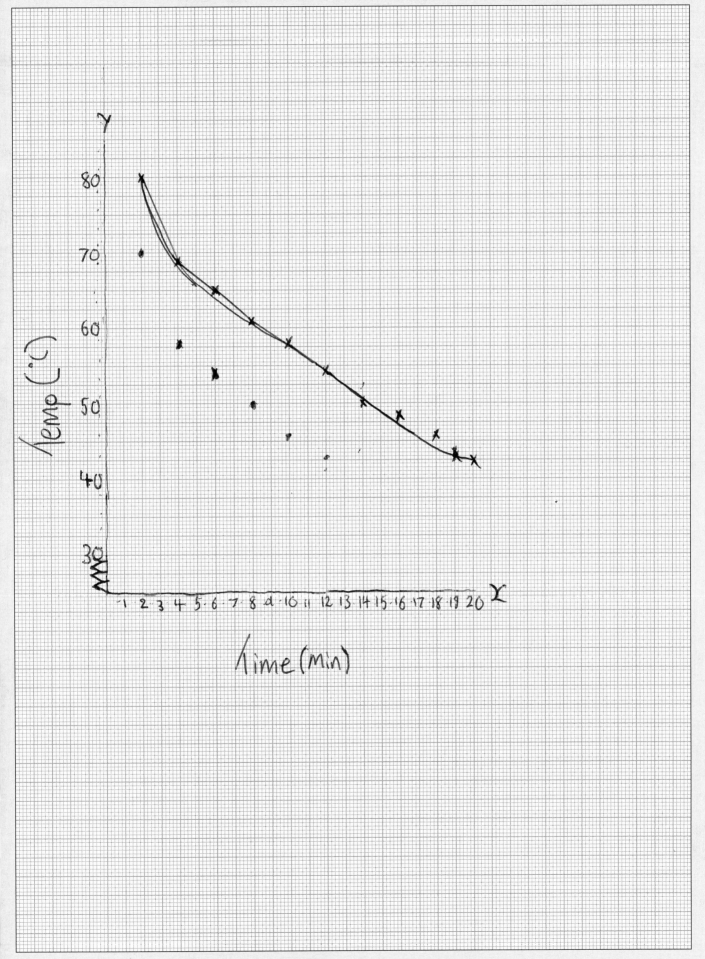

Considering your results/conclusions

3 Describe what your graph shows about the rate of cooling of the water in each tube.

4 Which colour is best at emitting radiation? Which is the worst? Explain your conclusion.

Evaluation

5 How well do your results support your conclusion? Your answer should refer to your graph.

6 Can you draw a general conclusion from your results (such as that light colours emit more radiation than dark colours)? Explain your answer.

Exam-style questions

1 Which part of the electromagnetic spectrum transfers energy by heating? **(1)**

....

2 Some very hot objects emit visible light. Explain why the water in the boiling tubes does not emit visible light. **(2)**

....

....

....

....

3 The world is getting warmer, which is causing many glaciers to melt faster than they used to. However, scientists have also discovered that deposits of soot and dust on the surface of ice in Greenland are causing the ice there to melt even more quickly.

a Explain what this report suggests about the difference in the amount of infrared radiation absorbed by light and dark surfaces. **(2)**

....

....

....

....

....

....

b Use your ideas about the way different coloured surfaces reflect visible light to suggest how the colour of a surface affects the amount of radiation it absorbs. **(3)**

....

....

....

....

....

....

....

....

....

....

Engineers who design circuits need to know the characteristics of different circuit components. Resistors are used to control the flow of current in a circuit but not all components keep the same resistance if the potential difference across them changes.

Your teacher may watch to see if you can:
- follow safety instructions to work safely
- make accurate measurements.

Task 1 – Investigating resistance
Method
A   Connect circuit X as shown in the diagram.

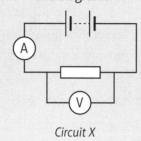

Circuit X

B   Set the power pack to a potential difference of 1 V and switch on. Record the readings on the ammeter and voltmeter in a table and then switch off.

C   Repeat step **B** for settings on the power pack of 2 V, 3 V, 4 V, 5 V and 6 V.

D   Replace the resistor in circuit X with a filament lamp. Repeat steps **B** and **C**.

Recording your results
1   Record your results for circuit X in the table below.

Potential difference (V)	Current (A)	
	Resistor	Filament lamp
0	0	0
1		
2		
3		
4		
5		
6		

Considering your results/conclusions

2 Plot a scatter diagram of your results. Plot the independent variable (potential difference) on the horizontal axis and the dependent variable (current) on the vertical axis. Use the same axes for both the resistor and the filament lamp. Draw two lines or curves of best fit, one through each set of points. Make sure you label the lines.

You can calculate the resistance from the potential difference and the current, using the equation on the right.

$$\text{resistance } (\Omega) = \frac{\text{potential difference (V)}}{\text{current (A)}}$$

3 **a** Calculate the resistance of the resistor when the potential difference is 1 V and when it is 6 V.

b Calculate the resistance of the filament lamp when the potential difference is 1 V and when it is 6 V.

c Draw a conclusion about how the resistance of the two components changes with increasing potential difference.

d Use evidence from your scatter diagram and your calculations to explain how you came to your conclusion.

Evaluation

4 **a** Looking at your scatter diagram for the resistor, how close were your points to the line of best fit?

b What does this tell you about the quality of data you have gathered?

5 How reproducible were your results? (Compare your results with other groups.)

Task 2 – Filament lamps in series and parallel circuits

Prediction

6 Look at circuits Y and Z below. Explain how you think the readings will compare in the two circuits for:

   a the ammeters   **b** the voltmeters.

....

....

....

Method

A Connect the circuit shown in circuit Y.

B Set the power pack to 1 V and switch on. Record the readings on the ammeter and the voltmeters, and then switch off.

C Repeat step **B** for settings on the power pack of 2 V, 3 V, 4 V, 5 V and 6 V.

D Now set up the circuit shown in circuit Z.

E Set the power pack to 1 V and switch on. Record the readings on the ammeters and the voltmeters, and then switch off.

F Repeat step **E** for settings on the power pack of 2 V, 3 V, 4 V, 5 V and 6 V.

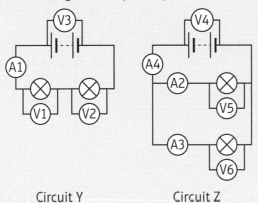

Circuit Y   Circuit Z

Aim

To test series and parallel circuits using resistors and filament lamps.

Apparatus

- power supply
- three voltmeters
- three ammeters
- connecting wires
- two crocodile clips
- two filament lamps

Safety ⚠

Never use mains electricity for practical work with circuits.

Ask your teacher to check your circuit before you switch it on.

Recording your results

7 Record your results for circuits Y and Z in the table below.

Potential difference (volts)	Circuit Y (lamps in series) ammeter (A) and voltmeter (V) readings				Circuit Z (lamps in parallel) ammeter (A) and voltmeter (V) readings					
	A1	V1	V2	V3	A2	A3	A4	V4	V5	V6
0	0	0	0	0	0	0	0	0	0	0
1										
2										
3										
4										
5										
6										

Considering your results/conclusions

8 a Compare the total current in the circuit through the two filament lamps when they are connected in series and when they are connected in parallel.

....

....

....

....

....

....

b Compare the potential difference across two filament lamps when they are connected in series and in parallel.

....

....

....

....

....

....

9 How does changing the potential difference across each circuit affect how these values compare?

....

....

....

....

....

....

Evaluation

10 Suggest what the answer would be to question **9** if fixed resistors replaced the lamps in the two circuits.

....

....

....

....

....

Exam-style questions

1 State the units for measuring resistance. **(1)**

....

2 Tables 1 and 2 show some results from the investigation on filament lamps in series and parallel circuits (shown in diagrams A and B).

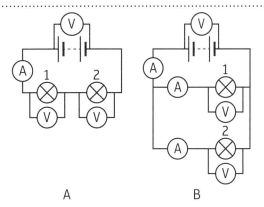

A   B

Table 1

	Potential difference (V)		
	Power pack	**Lamp 1**	**Lamp 2**
Series (A)	4	2	2
Parallel (B)	4	4	4

Table 2

	Current (A)		
	Power pack	**Lamp 1**	**Lamp 2**
Series (A)	0.23	(x)	(y)
Parallel (B)	(z)	0.41	0.41

a Explain what the current readings (x) and (y) would be. **(2)**

....

....

b Explain what the current reading (z) would be. **(2)**

....

....

3 a Use the information in tables 1 and 2 to calculate the overall resistance of:

  i circuit A **(2)**

....

  ii circuit B. **(2)**

....

b Describe how two bulbs can be put in a circuit to give the lowest possible overall resistance. **(1)**

....

....

Ships have a 'Plimsoll line' marked on them to show how far into the water they can sink without becoming unsafe. The safe level depends on the density of sea water.

Your teacher may watch to see if you can:
- take careful measurements.

Task 1 – Densities of solids
Method

A Find the mass of the solid. Write the name of the material and the mass of the object in a table.

B Stand a displacement can on the bench with its spout over a bowl. Fill the can with water until the water just starts to come out of the spout.

C Hold a measuring cylinder under the spout and carefully drop your object into the can.

D If your object floats, carefully push it down until all of it is under the water. Your finger should not be in the water.

E Stand the measuring cylinder on the bench and read the volume of water you have collected. This is the same as the volume of your object. Write the volume down.

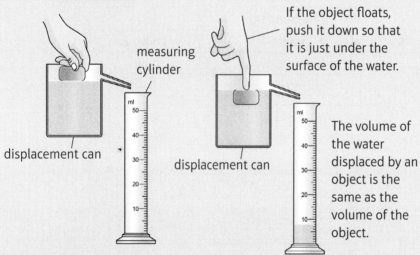

measuring cylinder

displacement can

displacement can

If the object floats, push it down so that it is just under the surface of the water.

The volume of the water displaced by an object is the same as the volume of the object.

Aim
To compare the densities of different liquids and solids.

Apparatus
• balance • displacement can • measuring cylinder • bowl • solids

Safety ⚠
Mop up any spills straight away.

Recording your results

1 Complete the table below.

Material	Mass (g)	Volume (cm³)	Density (g/cm³)

2 Calculate the density of each solid and write it in the table. The equation you need is:

$$\text{density (g/cm}^3) = \frac{\text{mass (g)}}{\text{volume (cm}^3)}$$

Task 2 – Densities of liquids

Method

A Put an empty beaker on a balance and zero the balance.

B Use a measuring cylinder to measure 50 cm³ of a liquid and pour it into the beaker. Write down the name of the liquid and the reading on the balance. This is the mass of 50 cm³ of the liquid.

Recording your results

3 Complete the table below.

Liquid	Mass of 50 cm³ (g)	Density (g/cm³)

4 Calculate the density of each liquid and write it in the table. The equation you need is:

$$\text{density (g/cm}^3) = \frac{\text{mass (g)}}{\text{volume (cm}^3)}$$

Apparatus

- balance
- measuring cylinder
- beaker
- liquids

Safety ⚠

Mop up any spills straight away.

Considering your results/conclusions

5 a What was the range of densities for the solids you measured?

....
....
....

b What was the range of densities for the liquids?

....
....
....

6 Compare the densities of the solids and liquids that you tested.

Exam-style questions

1 a Write down the equation for calculating the density of a substance. **(1)**

b Give suitable units for each of the quantities in the equation. **(1)**

2 A student found that the mass of 50 cm³ (0.000 05 m³) of cooking oil was 46 g.
Calculate the density of the cooking oil. Give your answer in kg/m³. **(3)**

3 A large piece of wood is 2 m long, 50 cm wide and 2 cm thick. It has a mass of 12 kg.
Calculate its density. **(3)**

4 A student uses the method in the practical that you have completed and works out that the density of pure water is 980 kg/m³. A textbook gives a value of 1000 kg/m³.
a Give a possible reason for the error in the student's result. **(1)**

b Describe a way of making the measurement of the density of fluids more accurate. **(1)**

Scientists monitoring the progress of glaciers need to understand the properties of water in its three forms: ice, liquid water and steam.

Your teacher may watch to see if you can:
- take careful measurements
- work safely.

Method

A Place a thermometer carefully into a boiling tube. Fill the boiling tube with crushed ice, and place the tube in a beaker. Adjust the position of the themometer so that its bulb is in the middle of the ice.

B Put the beaker onto a tripod and gauze. Pour hot water from a kettle into the beaker and keep it warm using a Bunsen burner.

C Measure the temperature of the ice every minute and record your results in a table. Stop taking readings three minutes after all the ice has melted.

D Note the time at which the ice starts to melt and the time when it appears to be completely melted.

Recording your results

1 Complete the table below.

Time (min)	Temperature (°C)

Considering your results/conclusions

2 Draw a line graph to show your results using the axes on the right. Mark on your graph the time when the ice started to melt and the time when it had completely melted.

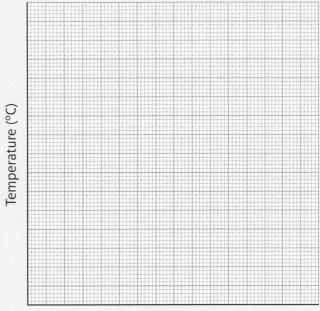

Temperature (°C)

Time (minutes)

Aim
To investigate how the temperature of ice changes as it melts.

Apparatus
- boiling tube
- beaker
- thermometer
- eye protection
- heat-resistant mat
- tripod and gauze
- Bunsen burner
- stop clock
- hot water
- crushed ice

Safety ⚠
Wear eye protection.
Take care when handling hot apparatus.

3 Describe the shape of your graph.

4 Explain the shape of your graph using ideas about the way particles are arranged in solids and liquids, and what happens to particles when the state of a substance changes.

Evaluation

5 a What sources of systematic error could be present in your results?

   b How could you avoid these errors?

6 a What sources of random error could there be in your results?

   b How could you avoid these errors?

Exam-style questions

1 Describe how the particles are arranged and held together in:

  a ice   **(2)**

....

....

....

....

....

....

  b liquid water.   **(2)**

....

....

....

....

....

2 The table shows a set of results from the melting ice investigation.
Plot a graph to present these results. Draw a line through the points. **(5)**

Time (min)	Temperature (°C)
0	−12
1	−8
2	−4
3	0
4	0
5	0
6	2
7	4
8	6

Your teacher may watch to see if you can:

- take careful measurements.

Method

A Put a polystyrene cup in a beaker onto a balance and zero the balance. Then fill the cup almost to the top with water and write down the mass of the water. Carefully remove the cup from the balance.

B Put a thermometer in the water and support it as shown in the diagram. Put a 12 V electric immersion heater into the water, making sure the heating element is completely below the water level. Connect the immersion heater to a joulemeter.

C Record the temperature of the water and then switch the immersion heater on. Stir the water in the cup gently using the thermometer.

D After five minutes, record the temperature of the water again and also write down the reading on the joulemeter.

Aim
To find the specific heat capacity of water.

Apparatus
- polystyrene cup
- beaker
- tripod
- thermometer
- stop clock
- immersion heater
- joulemeter
- balance

Recording your results

1 Record your results in this table.

Mass of water (g)	Mass of water (kg)	Starting temperature of water (°C)	Temperature after 5 minutes (°C)	Temperature change (°C)	Joulemeter reading (J)

Considering your results/conclusions

2 Divide the mass of water by 1000 to find the mass in kilograms.

3 Subtract the temperature of the water after five minutes from the starting temperature to find the change in temperature.

4 Calculate the specific heat capacity of water using this equation:

$$\text{specific heat capacity (J/kg°C)} = \frac{\text{change in thermal energy *(J)}}{\text{mass (kg)} \times \text{change in temperature (°C)}}$$

*Change in thermal energy is the same as energy transferred, and this is measured using the joulemeter.

....

Evaluation

5 Why did you use the glass beaker and the tripod?

....
....
....
....

6 Why did you put the water into a polystyrene cup instead of a beaker?

....
....
....
....

7 How would using a beaker have affected your results?

....
....
....
....

8 What are the possible sources of error in your investigation?

....
....
....
....

Exam-style questions

1 What does the specific heat capacity of a substance tell us about a substance? **(1)**

....

....

2 Sam heated 250 g of water in a polystyrene cup. The joulemeter reading was 11 kJ and the temperature change was 10 °C.

   a Calculate the specific heat capacity of water using the following equation:

$$\text{specific heat capacity (J/kg\,°C)} = \frac{\text{change in thermal energy (J)}}{\text{mass (kg)} \times \text{change in temperature (°C)}}$$ **(3)**

....

   b A textbook gives the specific heat capacity of water as 4181 J/kg °C.
      Suggest why you would expect Sam's result to be higher than this. **(3)**

....

....

....

....

   c Suggest how the method described above could be improved to reduce these errors. **(1)**

....

....

....

Designers need to know the characteristics of springs so that they can choose the best spring for their purpose.

Your teacher may watch to see if you can:
- take careful measurements.

Method

A Set up the apparatus as shown in the diagram. The zero on the ruler should be level with the bottom of the unstretched spring.

B Measure the length of the spring with no masses hanging on it and write it down.

C Hang a 100 g mass on the spring. Record the extension of the spring (the length shown on the ruler).

D Repeat step **C** until you have found the extension of the spring with 10 different masses. Each 100 g mass puts a downwards force of 1 N on the spring.

E Repeat steps **A**–**D** for a different spring.

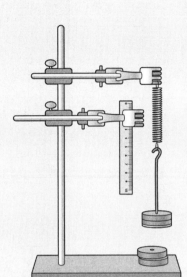

Aim
To investigate the extension and work done when applying forces to a spring.

Apparatus
- stand and two clamps
- springs
- ruler
- masses
- eye protection

Safety ⚠
Wear eye protection.

Recording your results

1 Draw a table like this to record your results.

Force (N)	Spring 1		Spring 2	
	Extension (cm)	Extension (m)	Extension (cm)	Extension (m)
0	0	0		
1				

2 Draw a scatter diagram to show force in newtons against extension in metres. Put extension on the horizontal axis and force on the vertical axis. Plot points for all your springs on the same diagram and join them with lines of best fit.

Considering your results/conclusions

3 Which of your springs feel the stiffest? (Which ones take more force to pull them?)

4 Calculate the gradient of the line on your diagram for each spring. The gradient gives you the spring constant for each spring. The spring constant gives a measure of how stiff a spring is: the larger the spring constant, the stiffer the spring.

5   How can you work out which springs should feel the stiffest by looking at their spring constants?

....

....

....

....

....

....

6   The work done to stretch a spring can be calculated using the following equation:

energy transferred in stretching (J) = $\frac{1}{2}$ × spring constant (N/m) × extension² (m)²

Calculate the energy transferred in stretching each of the springs that you tested.

....

Exam-style questions

1   **a** When a force moves an object, the work done in moving the object can be calculated using the equation: work done = force × distance.

     Explain why this equation cannot be used to calculate the work done in stretching a spring.   **(2)**

....

....

....

....

  b A spring has an extension of 0.5 m when there is a force of 20 N pulling on it. Calculate the spring constant, and then calculate the energy transferred in stretching this spring.   **(4)**

....

2   A student carried out the investigation described, adding 10 N to the spring between each measurement. The spring stretched by only 1 mm with 10 N hanging on it.

  a Describe how this might affect the accuracy of the results.   **(2)**

....

....

....

....

  b Explain how the method could be modified to improve the accuracy of the student's results.   **(2)**

....

....

....

....

well done

Equations in the left hand column are ones you may be asked to *recall and apply* in your exam.

You do not need to recall the equations in the right hand column, but you should be able to select and apply them in an exam.

Equations for Higher tier only are marked with the Higher icon.

Recall and apply	Select and apply
Unit SP1 Motion	
distance travelled = average speed × time $$d = x \times t$$ acceleration = change in velocity ÷ time taken $$a = \frac{(v - u)}{t}$$	(final velocity)² – (initial velocity)² = 2 × acceleration × distance $$v^2 - u^2 = 2 \times a \times s$$
Unit SP2 Motion and forces	
force = mass × acceleration $$F = m \times a$$ weight = mass × gravitational field strength $$W = m \times g$$ **H** momentum = mass × velocity $$p = m \times v$$ work done = force × distance moved in the direction of the force $$E = F \times d$$ kinetic energy = $\frac{1}{2}$ × mass × (speed)² $$KE = \frac{1}{2} \times m \times v^2$$	**H** force = change in momentum ÷ time $$F = \frac{(mv - mu)}{t}$$
Unit SP3 Conservation of energy	
change in gravitational potential energy = mass × gravitational field strength × change in vertical height $$GPE = m \times g \times h$$ efficiency = $\frac{\text{useful energy transferred by the device}}{\text{total energy supplied to the device}}$	
Unit SP4 Waves	
wave speed = frequency × wavelength $$v = f \times \lambda$$ wave speed = distance ÷ time $$v = \frac{x}{t}$$	
Unit SP8 Energy – Forces doing work	
power = work done ÷ time taken $$P = \frac{E}{t}$$	
Unit SP9 Forces and their effects	
moment of a force = force × distance normal to the direction of the force	

Biology, Chemistry & Physics

Recall and apply	Select and apply

Unit SP10 Electricity and circuits

charge = current × time

$$Q = I \times t$$

energy transferred = charge moved × potential difference

$$E = Q \times V$$

potential difference = current × resistance

$$V = I \times R$$

power = energy transferred ÷ time taken

$$P = \frac{E}{t}$$

electrical power = current × potential difference

$$P = I \times V$$

electrical power = current squared × resistance

$$P = I^2 \times R$$

Select and apply

energy transferred = current × potential difference × time

$$E = I \times V \times t$$

Unit SP12 Magnetism and the motor effect

H force on a conductor = magnetic × current × length
at right angles to   flux density
a magnetic field
carrying a current

$$F = B \times I \times l$$

Unit SP13 Electromagnetic induction

H $$\frac{\text{potential difference across primary coil}}{\text{potential difference across secondary coil}} = \frac{\text{number of turns in primary coil}}{\text{number of turns in secondary coil}}$$

$$\frac{V_p}{V_s} = \frac{N_p}{N_s}$$

For transformers with 100% efficiency,

potential difference across primary coil × current in primary coil = potential difference across secondary coil × current in secondary coil

$$V_p \times I_p = V_s \times I_s$$

Unit SP14 Particle model

density = mass ÷ volume

$$\rho = \frac{m}{V}$$

Select and apply

change in thermal energy = mass × specific heat capacity × change in temperature

$$\Delta Q = m \times c \times \Delta \theta$$

thermal energy for a change of state = mass × specific latent heat

$$Q = M \times L$$

to calculate pressure or volume for gases of fixed mass at constant temperature

$$P_1 \times V_1 = P_2 \times V_2$$

Unit SP15 Forces and matter

force exerted on a spring = spring constant × extension

$$F = k \times x$$

pressure = force normal to surface ÷ area of surface

$$P = \frac{F}{A}$$

Select and apply

energy transferred in stretching = 0.5 × spring constant × (extension)^2

$$E = \frac{1}{2} \times k \times x^2$$

H pressure due to a column of liquid = height of column × density of liquid × gravitational field strength

$$P = h \times \rho \times g$$

BIOLOGY
SB1b
Exam-style questions

1 a The lens makes things appear two times bigger (1).

b $2 \times 7 = \times14$, $5 \times 7 = \times35$, $10 \times 7 = \times70$ (3).

2 diameter of 10 cells is 0.2 mm, so diameter of one cell = 0.2/10 = 0.02 mm (2: 1 for working, 1 for correct answer with units).

3 a $0.45 \times 500 = 225$ mm (or 22.5 cm) (1).

b $0.1 \times 500 = 50$ mm (or 5 cm) (1).

SB1f

1 The results will depend on the particular food supplied and tested. The table below shows some typical results:

Food	Iodine test	Benedict's test	Biuret test	Emulsion test
full-fat milk	yellow–orange	yellow	purple	cloudy
whey	yellow–orange	bright blue	purple	clear
egg white	yellow–orange	bright blue	purple	clear
potato	black–blue	bright blue	light blue	clear
glucose	yellow–orange	red precipitate	light blue	clear
(icing sugar)	yellow–orange	bright blue	light bue	clear

2 Answers depend on the particular food supplied and tested.

3 Both the test for reducing sugars and proteins could give an indication depending on the colour produced. For reducing sugar, the colour change from light blue (no reducing sugar) to green/blue then orange and eventually red (lots of reducing sugar) indicates the amount of reducing sugar present. For the protein test, a colour change is an indication where the darker the purple colour produced, the more protein present.

4 This will depend on the results obtained if they were not as expected. Errors are most likely to occur if equipment is not cleaned properly between tests and it becomes contaminated with another sample. Therefore it would be a good idea to ensure equipment (i.e. glassware, spatulas etc.) is cleaned between tests. Using coloured foods may also make some colour changes more difficult to see. To overcome this problem there would be a need to select food that have more neutral or muted colours.

Exam-style questions

1 a starch (1)

b protein (1)

c fat or oil/lipid (1)

d reducing sugar (1)

2 Check the hazard information for any reagents used (1).

3 a Blue/black (1) because rice contains a lot of starch (1).

b Blue (1) because egg white contains no reducing sugar (1).

c Purple (1) because egg white contains protein (1).

d Cloudy emulsion (1) because cheese contains fat/lipid (1).

SB1h

1 Your own prediction and explanation.

2 Your own table.

3 Your own data.

4 Your own graph.

5 Your own results.

6 Your own results.

7 Your own results.

8 Your own results.

9 Your own results.

10 Your own results.

Exam-style questions

1 a Gas syringe (1) with any suitable reason, such as some of the oxygen might dissolve in water (if the upturned measuring cylinder was used), or the scale on the syringe might be finer so giving more accurate readings (1).

b Use a pH meter (1) because:
- universal/pH indicator solution might interfere with the reaction
- OR a pH meter is more accurate
- OR universal/pH indicator is not accurate/sensitive enough to distinguish between small pH increments.

c Graph drawn from data in table:
- axes drawn with suitable scales and labelled appropriately (1)
- points plotted accurately and joined by one curved line for each pH (1)
- both lines drawn on same axes (1).

d Measurement taken at 4 mins for pH 6 is too low compared to the rest of the results (1). Any suitable reason that explains the low result, such as scale was not read accurately (1).

e 10.6 cm³ produced in 6 mins = $\frac{10.6}{6}$ = 1.77 cm³/min.

2 a Bacterium A: pH 4 (1); bacterium B: pH 2 (1).

b The enzyme from bacterium A (1) because it takes less time to break down the substrate than the enzyme from bacterium B (1).

c Bacterium A (1) because its optimum pH is the most acidic (1).

SB1i

1 Your own predictions and explanations.

2 Your own table.

3 Your own results.

4 Your own results.

5 Your own results.

6 Your own results.

7 Your own graph.

8 Your own graph.

9 Your own graph.

10 The percentage change in mass gives an indication of the overall movement of molecules between the potato strips and the solution.

11 A mean value is likely to 'iron out' any variations in the way the experiment was carried out.

12 Your own results.

Exam-style questions

1 a 0% + 0.09 g; 10% – 0.26 g; 30% – 0.55 g; 50% – 1.17 g (1 mark for correct values, 1 mark for units and correctly identifying gain or loss).

b 0% + 1.9%; 10% – 5.0%; 30% – 11.1%; 50% – 24.1% (1 mark for correct values, 1 mark for units and correctly identifying gain or loss).

c The slice gained mass because osmosis took place into the root from the surrounding water (1).

d All the slices lost mass, but the percentage loss in mass increases as the solution concentration increases (1). This is because osmosis happens faster as the difference in concentration between the potato tissue and solution increases (1).

e A concentration equivalent to between 0% and 10% sucrose solution (1), because when the concentrations are equal there will be no change in mass (1).

f Any suitable suggestion that identifies how accuracy can be increased, such as using a range of solutions between 0% and 10% (1).

2 a The potato lost water fastest (1), because the gradient of its line is steeper than for the halophyte (1).

b Potato has a lower solute concentration inside its cells than the halophyte (1), so will lose water faster by osmosis than the halophyte when placed in a concentrated solution (1).

c Rate of change = $\frac{-8.2}{6}$ = –1.4% per minute (1).

SB5k

1 Your own measurements.

2 Your own results.

3 Your own drawing.

4 Your own results.

5 a Your own results.

b Your own results.

6 Any sensible suggestions and reasons.

7 **a** C, F, G, H, I, J, K, L, M, N, O, P
   b Working aseptically means that cultures are not contaminated.

Exam-style questions

1 **a** All of their results are lower than those of the other groups (1).
   b and **c** Any suitable suggestion that accounts for all results being lower, such as:
   • didn't measure the radius of the spaces correctly
   • used the wrong equation to calculate the cross-sectional area.

2 As the concentration of the antibiotic increases, (1) the cross-sectional area of bacteria that are killed also increases (1).

3 Penicillin G 6.15 cm² (1); methicillin 0.007 cm² (1); streptomycin 10.17 cm² (1).

4 Streptomycin is more effective than penicillin G at killing *Micrococcus luteus* bacteria (1) and methicillin has hardly any effect on the bacteria (1).

SB6b

1 Your own results.
2 **a** Your own results. **b** Your own results.
3 Your own results.
4 **a** Your own results. **b** Your own results.
5 The part of an experiment in which the *independent* variable is not applied is called the control. A control is used to check that the *independent* variable has an effect (and that the effect is not due to another variable). In this experiment, the independent variable is the *light* intensity. The control is the *tube covered in foil*. We know that the independent variable has a direct effect on the final pH of the indicator because *when light could not get to the algae, the indicator colour did not change* [or words to that effect].

Exam-style questions

1 **a** At about 2 minutes – after this time, oxygen concentration rises, as it is produced by photosynthesis when it is light (1).
   b At about 13 minutes – after this time, oxygen concentration falls, as photosynthesis stops producing it and respiration uses it up (1).
   c Working shown (2) to work out the gradient of the line of best fit, e.g.:
   $$\frac{5.96 - 5.3}{12 - 2.5} = \frac{0.66}{9.5} = 0.07 \text{ mg/dm}^3/\text{min (1)}$$
   d $y = 0.07 \times 4.2 + 5.1$ (2) $= 5.4$ mg dm³ (1)
   e Photosynthesis needs light (1), and the greater the light intensity (1), the faster the rate of photosynthesis (1).
   f The light intensity is not the limiting factor (1) /something else is a limiting factor (1).
   g Either increase carbon dioxide concentration or increase temperature (1).

SB8e

1 Your own results.
2 Your own results.
3 **a** The temperature.
   b The distance moved by the coloured liquid.
   c One of: the number of organisms, the length of time that the coloured liquid was observed to move.
   d The number of organisms – because the higher number you have, the higher the rate of respiration (or vice versa with a lower number); the length of time – because this will not allow you to compare readings if the timing is different.
   e The greater the temperature, the faster the rate of respiration.
   f Chemical reactions occur more quickly at higher temperatures.
4 **a** oxygen
   b carbon dioxide
   c it is absorbed by the soda lime.

Exam-style questions

1 Not below freezing (since this may harm the cells of the maggots) (1 mark – for both the temperature and the reason). Not above 40 °C (accept a range of 30–45 °C) since maggots are unlikely to experience these temperatures in reality/their enzymes may start to denature/may cause injury to the maggots (1 mark – for both the temperature and the reason).

2 **a** To increase the likelihood that the results are correct (1).
   b Correctly plotted points (1) scatter diagram with suitable axes and labels (1).
   c 30 °C, 10 mm (1).
   d A leak in the container allowing air into it, **or** starting the stop clock to time too late/stopping it too early (1).
   e Line of best fit (1).
   f The higher the temperature, the greater the rate of respiration/the faster the coloured liquid blob moves (1).
   g At higher temperatures, organisms/enzymes are more active (1), so more respiration is needed to release energy (1).

SB9b

1 Your own results.
2 Your own results.
3 Your own results.
4 Your own results.
5 Your own results.
6 Your own results.
7 Your own results.

Exam-style questions

1 Quadrats placed along the transect will record changes in presence/absence or changes in abundance from one area to another (1).

2 Factors caused by physical and chemical differences in the environment (1).

3 Any two suitable abiotic factors with a reason (max. 2 marks, 1 for each factor), such as:
   • light intensity will be greater in open ground than under the tree, because of shading by tree canopy
   • air humidity may be greater under the tree than in open air, because it is cooler and there is less wind under the tree
   • soil moisture may be greater in open ground than under the tree, because tree roots absorb a lot of moisture and canopy shelters ground
   • air temperature may vary more above open ground than under the tree because the tree canopy provides shelter.

4 Any answer which indicates that different species are adapted to different habitats (1), and so distribution and abundance will be affected by abiotic factors that vary from their preferred habitat (1).

5 **a** Light intensity and temperature (and other related factors) will vary with amount of shade (1), and the size and position of the tree's shadow will change with time of day (1).
   b Some areas will be under the tree's shadow at some parts of the day and not others, so measurements of abiotic factors at one time of day may not reflect what that area experiences most of the day (1), and so may give a false conclusion (1).

CHEMISTRY
SC2d.1

1 The liquid you have produced (the distillate) will be clear and colourless, the ink colour should not appear in the distillate.

2 The answer should be around 100 °C as this is the boiling point of water; however, values slightly below 100 °C are acceptable providing the reason given links to impurities.

3 To keep the test tube cool (and condense the vapour back into a liquid).

4 **a** The glass might smash and therefore there are risk of cuts; boiling water could spill and risk of this going onto clothes and skin; people could slip due to spilt water on the floor.
   b Stand up while doing practical work; so that you can more easily move out of the way; along with making sure that the tripod is stable and that the flask is steady; use a clamp and stand to secure the flask in place.

5 Any suitable hazard; together with one way of reducing the risk – e.g. hazard from liquid boiling over; reducing the risk could include the use of anti-bumping granules.

6 **a** Air hole closed (yellow flame); makes the flame more visible (luminous); so reducing the risk of someone touching the flame accidentally.
   b Air hole slightly/half open; gas tap turned about half on; makes sure heating is gentle; helping to reduce the risk of the liquid boiling over and avoids depositing soot onto the gauze/flask.

7   Your answer should refer to your actual results and how well this compared to the success criteria you set out in Q1 above. Possible tests for water could be: adding the distillate to anhydrous copper sulfate which turns blue (with water) or using cobalt chloride paper which turns purple/pink (with water).

8   Your answer should include:
   • ink/liquid is heated until it boils
   • liquid/water evaporates and turns into steam, also known as water vapour
   • steam is pure water vapour, so the temperature reading on the thermometer is 100 °C
   • the steam/vapour passes into the condenser, where it cools down
   • when it cools it turns from a vapour/gas back into a liquid
   • the pure water collects as the distillate.

Exam-style questions

1   a   It becomes darker (1) because it becomes more concentrated/solvent leaves the ink but the coloured substances do not (1).
    b   The solvent was not pure/it was a mixture of liquids (1).

2   Solvent has a lower boiling point than the solute/solvent is liquid, but solute is solid at room temperature (1); solvent boils and leaves the solution (1); solvent vapour is cooled and condensed away from the solution (1).

3   Heat the liquid until it boils (1); measure its boiling point (1); pure water boils at 100 °C (1).

SC2d.2

1   You should have correctly identified different colours in the inks you tested.

2   You should have correctly measured from the pencil line to where the solvent reached.

3   You should have completed the middle rows of your results table.

4   You should have completed the bottom row of your results table; you needed to use the formula to work out the R_f values.

5   This is dependent on your results; you need to look for any black inks which did not separate into a number of colours – the ink just remained as one main dot. Remember, the inks must have moved otherwise they would be insoluble in water.

6   Again, this is dependent on your results. However, similar coloured dyes (in the same location) on your chromatography paper are likely to contain the same chemical compound.

7   The graphite from the pencil will not dissolve in the solvent (water) and so will not interfere with the results. This will also help when working out the R_f values, as there will be a clear point to take measurements from.

8   This was done so you could easily recall which pen/original colour of ink was used to produce each spot of ink.

9   The water rises up the paper, and dissolves the dyes.

10   This was done to stop the dyes washing out of the paper.

11   The answer will depend on how clear the top level of each dye is on your chromatograms; if it is difficult to identify the top of each dye accurately, then the accuracy and reliability of the calculated R_f values will be reduced.

Exam-style questions

1   a   Propanone (1).
    b   Paper (1).
    c   She should avoid flames because propanone is flammable (1).
    d   The ink would dissolve into the propanone/wash out of the paper (1).

2   The solvent (**or** liquid/mobile phase) (1) moves through the paper (**or** stationary phase) (1), taking the soluble substances with it at different rates (1).

3   a   Ink X is a mixture of inks B and C (1) and does not contain ink A (1).
    b   You would need to use this formula:
    $$R_f = \frac{\text{distance moved by the compound}}{\text{distance moved by the solvent}}$$
    and either measure the distances on the chromatogram or use the scale at the side.
    R_f = 0.75 (1 mark for substitution in formula, 1 mark for final answer)

SC8c

1   The crystals are blue and diamond shaped. (The size will vary depending on conditions.)

2   a   clear solution
    b   black solid (powder)
    c   blue solution

3   copper oxide + sulfuric acid → copper sulfate + water

4   So that all the acid is used up.

5   The acid would react with the excess copper oxide and some or all of it would disappear.

6   Copper oxide.

7   Copper sulfate.

8   Because the hydrogen ions of the acid are removed (and a salt and water are formed).

9   Copper oxide.

10   $CuO(s) + H_2SO_4(aq) \rightarrow CuSO_4(aq) + H_2O(l)$

Exam-style questions

1   Because it is formed by the reaction between a base and an acid (1).

2   The copper oxide is a solid (made up of larger particles) that gets stuck in the filter paper (1). The particles of the copper sulfate are in solution (smaller) so pass through the filter paper (1).

3   a   nickel oxide + hydrochloric acid → nickel chloride + water (1)
    b $NiO(s) + 2HCl(aq)$ (1) $\rightarrow NiCl_2(aq) + H_2O(l)$ (1)
    c   Step 1: add excess nickel oxide to some (dilute) hydrochloric acid (1).
    Step 2: filter out excess nickel oxide (1).
    Step 3: evaporate water to leave nickel chloride (1).

4   Small crystals are produced by fast evaporation of the water in the solution (1). Large crystals are produced by slow evaporation of the water in the solution (1).

SC8d

1   Suitable table drawn: two columns; first column labelled mass of $Ca(OH)_2$ power added/(g); second column labelled pH of the mixture; sufficient rows for nine readings.

2   Graph plotted with pH on vertical axis, mass of $Ca(OH)_2$ added (g) on horizontal axis; curve of best fit drawn; suitable title included.

3   Expected results: pH increases as more calcium hydroxide is added; end-point is 1.85 g; solubility of $Ca(OH)_2$ is about 0.17 g per 100 cm³ H_2O; so beyond this excess $Ca(OH)_2$ is seen.

4   Intercept at pH 7 identified; mass read from graph.

5   Improvement suggested, e.g. use more precuse balance (±0.01 g or ±0.001 g); increase volume of acid used; use narrow range indicator paper; use pH meter.

Exam-style questions

1   a   calcium chloride (1)
    b $Ca(OH)_2(aq) + 2HCl(aq) \rightarrow CaCl_2(aq) + 2H_2O(l)$ 1 mark for formulae, 1 mark for balancing, 1 mark for state symbols

2   To avoid damage to eyes (1) because hydrochloric acid is irritant/corrosive (1).

3   a   Volume of acid (1); concentration of acid (1).
    b   pH of reaction mixture (1).
    c   Use a thermometer instead of indicator paper or a pH meter (1).

4   a   To make sure that it gives an accurate pH value / pH value close to the true value (1).
    b   The pH meter has the higher resolution because it gives readings to 1 or 2 decimal places (1) but universal indicator paper only gives readings to the nearest whole pH unit (1).

SC10a

1   Your table should be complete, including the columns showing the change in mass.

2   Your scatter diagram should show change in mass of electrode on the vertical axis and current on the horizontal axis; these axes need to be labelled (including units). You should have chosen a suitable scale that enables the scatter diagram to be as large as possible, and the points need to be plotted correctly with a line of best fit which is straight. The line for the anode should show a decrease in mass and the line for the cathode should show an increase in mass as the current increases.

3 For the anode: the decrease in mass is directly proportional to the current, **or** as the current increases, the decrease in mass increases proportionally.
For the cathode: the increase in mass is directly proportional to the current, **or** as the current increases, the increase in mass increases proportionally.

4 Anode: copper atoms lose electrons to form copper ions; the copper ions dissolve in the solution, **or** $Cu(s) \rightarrow Cu^{2+}(aq) + 2e$
Cathode: copper ions gain electrons to form copper; which sticks to the surface of the cathode, **or** $Cu^{2+}(aq) + 2e \rightarrow Cu(s)$

5 Your prediction needs to have been made by reading from 0.35 A on the horizontal axis, reading/drawing a line up to the best fit line for the **anode** you drew and then reading/drawing a line across to the change in mass of electrode on the vertical axis.

6 Some of the deposited copper does not stick to the cathode, so the cathode does not gain as much mass as expected, **or** there are impurities in the anode and they fall to the bottom of the beaker, so the anode appears to lose more mass.

7 You would need to repeat the experiment and take an average of the concordant results.

8 At the anode: bubbles of a colourless gas, product is oxygen
At the cathode: covered with a layer of brown metal, product is copper.

9 Hydroxide ions from the water are attracted to the anode; they lose electrons to form oxygen and water.
Copper ions are attracted to the cathode; they gain two electrons to form copper.

10 Ⓗ $4OH^- \rightarrow O_2 + 2H_2O + 4e$ oxidation
$Cu^{2+} + 2e \rightarrow Cu$ reduction

Exam-style questions

1 As it is a four mark question, four statements are needed in order to gain full marks. The answer should include:
- sulfate and hydroxide ions are attracted to the anode during electrolysis (1)
- and hydroxide ions are more readily discharged than sulfate ions (1)
- so oxygen is produced (1)
- as there are no copper atoms in the graphite electrode to form ions (1).

2 a Any sensible precaution would be allowed (1), but typical answers could be:
- wear eye protection, to prevent copper sulfate solution splashing into eyes
- ensure no naked flames when using propanone, as it is flammable
- ensure the power supply does not go above 6 V, to prevent the connecting wires and electrodes from getting too hot.
b So that the copper deposited will adhere to the cathode (1).
c The current may vary during the experiment and the variable resistor can be used to keep the current constant (1).
d To remove the copper sulfate solution (1).
e To help the electrodes to dry more quickly as it evaporates quickly (1).

SC14d

1 Your own results.

2 Work out the mean (average) titre taken from results that are within 0.2 cm³. To do this select results within 0.2 cm³ of each other and divide by the number of results used.

3 Moles of NaOH = (25.0 ÷ 1000) × 0.10 = 0.0025

4 Number of moles of HCl = 0.0025.
The number of moles of HCl will be the same as the previous answer as the ratio is 1:1 and this can be seen in the balanced symbol equation.

5 Concentration HCl = (0.0025 ÷ mean volume HCl) × 1000 (or convert cm³ to dm³ before doing the calculation in which case there is no need to multiply by 1000).

Exam-style questions

1 To remove any water or other solution left in them from previous use.

2 To make it easier to see the colour change of the indicator.

3 The point in the neutralisation when the indicator just changes colour.

4 a 25.30 cm³.
b 25.20 cm³ (1) because it is the average of the concordant values (1).
c A description including the following points: repeat the titration using 25 cm³ of sodium hydroxide solution and the volume of hydrochloric acid calculated in **b** but no indicator/methyl orange (1); pour the solution into an evaporating basin (1); heat the solution/leave the solution until all of the water has evaporated (1).
d Ⓗ   Number of moles of NaOH used
$$= 0.100 \times \frac{25.0}{1000} = 0.00250 \, mol \ (1)$$
number of moles of HCl used = 0.00250 (1)
concentration of HCl
$$= 0.0025 \times \frac{1000}{25.20} = 0.0992 \, mol \, dm^{-3} \ (1).$$

SC18b.1

1 If results are good, the scatter diagram should show two curves rising steadily and levelling off at about the same point. The curve for the small chips should rise and level off more quickly.

2 The reactions had finished when the scatter diagrams levelled off.

3 For a fixed mass of chips, the smaller the chips, the larger the surface area (to volume ratio).

4 The larger the surface area (to volume ratio), the faster the reaction.

5 The scatter diagram for larger surface area to volume ratio (smaller chips) rises more quickly at the start and levels off more quickly. Therefore, the larger the surface area, the faster the reaction.

6 If the results are good, the scatter diagram should show a straight line rising steadily as the concentration increases.

7 The higher the concentration of the acid, the faster the reaction.

8 The scatter diagram for volume of gas produced in one minute against concentration rises steadily. Therefore, the higher the concentration, the faster the reaction.

9 Possible sources of error are: measuring the volume of gas (which is difficult because of the bubbles in the measuring cylinder), and making sure the marble chips are all the same size. (Other answers possible.)

10 Measure the volume of gas produced for a longer time, or measure larger volumes of gas. (Other answers possible.)

11 Possible sources of error are: measuring the volume of gas (which is difficult because of the bubbles in the measuring cylinder), and making sure the marble chips are all the same size. (Other answers possible.)

12 Measure the volume of gas produced for a longer time or measure larger volumes of gas. (Other answers possible.)

Exam-style questions

1 The electronic balance could be used to measure the change in mass (1) of the reactants (and flask/beaker) as the reaction proceeds (1). The faster the loss in mass, the faster the reaction (1).

2 a It is finished in 5 minutes (1), as at this point the graph levels off, which means no more gas is being formed (1).
b The graph for the smaller chips would have a similar shape to the graph for large chips (1), but would rise faster and level off at the same point, more quickly than the given large chips graph (1).
c The average rate = 40/5 (1) = 8 cm³/min (1).
d Find the point on the curve at 100 seconds, and draw the tangent line to the curve at the point (1). Choose two points on the tangent line where it is easy to read the time and volume, and calculate the change in volume that occurs for that change in time (1). Calculate the rate by dividing the change in the volume by the change in time (1).

SC18b.2

1 There should be a completed table of results with two columns: one for temperature, and the other for the time taken for the cross to disappear. The correct units should also be clearly displayed in the table.

2 The scatter diagram should show a curve, with time decreasing quickly as temperature increases.

3 a The rate increases quickly as the temperature increases.

b The scatter diagram shows that as the temperature rises, the time for the reaction decreases; this means the rate of reaction increases.

4 The time taken would halve.

5 a 10 °C.

b You need to mark on your scatter diagram a particular temperature – for example, 40 °C. From this you draw a line to the time taken axis and make a note of this value. You need to halve this time; for example, if your result was 60 seconds, you need to look at the temperature at 30 seconds. From this, you should be able to see a temperature difference of about 10 °C.

6 Any two of the following measurements: temperature, time and volume of solutions.

7 Errors with recording temperature and time could be reduced by repeating the experiment more often. Errors with measuring volume of solution could be reduced by using burettes and/or pipettes. (Other answers possible.)

Exam-style questions

1 The powdered chalk has a larger surface area to volume ratio than the lumps of chalk (1). This means more collisions occur between the acid particles and the chalk (1). More collisions mean that the reaction occurs more quickly (1).

2 a The cross disappears because the precipitate (solid) settles at the bottom of the flask (1).

b Vertical axis: 'Time for cross to disappear (s)' (1); horizontal axis: 'Average temperature (°C)' (1); sketch shows line starting high and curving downwards, getting less steep as it gets closer to the horizontal axis (1).

c As the temperature increases the time taken decreases (1), so the reaction is getting quicker as less time is needed to get to the same point (an approximate 10 °C rise in temperature halves the time taken, so doubles the reaction rate) (1).

d By repeating the experiment (at the same temperatures) and averaging the results (1).

SC23b

1 Your own results.

2 Your own results.

3 a The results should show that the mass of alcohol needed to produce a 1 °C rise in temperature decreases down the group of alcohols (as the number of carbon atoms in the alcohol increases).

b The alcohols show a trend in properties because there is a regular increase in the size of their molecular structure.

4 Any four from:
- loss of heat to surroundings,
- heat transferred by heating up equipment, measuring temperatures,
- measuring mass of water,
- measuring mass of alcohol burned,
- evaporation of alcohol and evaporation of water.

The main error would arise from heat losses, as most of the heat produced will be transferred to the surroundings.

Exam-style questions

1 a The flask containing water will need to be placed at the same height above the flame each time (1).

b To prevent heat loss (1); so the energy released goes into heating up the water (1).

c Do not pour alcohols near naked flames/take care not to spill the contents of the burners (1).

2 0.03 g (1)

SC25c.1

1 The metal ions in unknown solids correctly identified using your own flame test results. Your teacher will have the correct results for you to double check.

2 To remove any substance remaining from the previous test that may affect the flame colour seen in new test.

3 There are a number of possible difficulties that could be stated.
- faint flame colour so it was difficult to distinguish the colour
- substances dropped into the Bunsen making it difficult to see subsequent results
- unknown samples becoming more contaminated as tests went on.

It is also possible that no difficulty was encountered. However, you need to state how you knew this. A simple explanation and reason could be that you had no difficulties as you correctly identified the metal ions in all of the four unknown solids.

Exam-style questions

1 1 mark for each correctly matched cation and colour up to 5 marks: lithium – red; sodium – yellow; potassium – lilac; calcium – orange-red; copper – blue-green.

2 a Two of the following for 1 mark each: does not colour the flame; high melting point/does not melt; does not react with air/unreactive

b The flame is already coloured/the flame test colour is difficult to see/the flame is not hot enough (1).

c To remove traces of the previous substance (1); so that the flame colour is not affected (1).

SC25c.2

1 Your own results.

2 Metal ions in unknown solutions correctly identified using your results. Your teacher will have the correct results for you to double check.

3 Aluminium ions and calcium ions both produce white precipitates; step D is an extra test to distinguish between them; aluminium hydroxide disappears in excess sodium hydroxide solution, but calcium hydroxide does not.

Exam-style questions

1 a 1 mark for each correctly matched cation and colour up to 3 marks: copper – blue; iron(II) – green; iron(III) – brown.

b Add excess sodium hydroxide solution (1); only aluminium hydroxide dissolves to form a colourless solution (1).

SC25c.3

1 The anions in 'unknown' solutions correctly identified using your own results. Your teacher will have the correct results for you to double check.

2 The acid reacts with carbonate ions; so silver carbonate and barium carbonate cannot form; these would interfere with the results of the tests or would produce false positive results.

Exam-style questions

1 1 mark for each correctly matched ion and colour up to 3 marks: chloride – white; bromide – cream; iodide – yellow.

2 Bubble the gas through limewater (1); which turns milky/cloudy white (1).

3 a To react with carbonate ions so they are removed/to react with substances that would also form a white precipitate with silver nitrate (1).

b Hydrochloric acid contains chloride ions (1); which would form silver chloride/give a false positive test for chloride ions (1).

PHYSICS

SP2d

1 Your own results.

2 Your own results.

3 Your own results.

4 Your own results.

5 Your own results.

6 a Acceleration decreases as mass increases. (Acceleration is inversely proportional to mass, although you cannot determine that the relationship *is* one of inverse proportion without plotting a graph of acceleration against 1/mass and obtaining a straight line.).

b Your own prediction.

7 a Your own results.

b Your own results.

8 Your own results.

9 Your own results.

Exam-style questions

1 Acceleration is a change in speed over time (1), so find the difference in the two speeds and divide by the time taken to move between the two light gates (1).

2 The acceleration is proportional to the force (1).

3 a The acceleration gets less as the mass increases (1). *You should not write 'the acceleration is inversely proportional to the mass' at this point, as this cannot be determined for certain from the shape of the graph.*

  b Plot acceleration against 1/mass (or mass against 1/acceleration) (1); if this is a straight line it will show that the acceleration is inversely proportional to the accelerating mass (1).

SP4b.1

1 Your own results.

2 Your own results.

3 Results may vary because of different water depths (and different frequencies/wavelengths for the measurement of the series of waves).

4 There may be less than one wave in a second/any errors in counting the waves are spread out over 10 s, so this will give a more accurate value.

5 Comments are likely to mention the difficulty of measuring the wavelength while the waves were moving. The camera 'freezes' the motion of the waves so it is easier to take a precise and accurate measurement.

6 Comments are likely to relate to the speed of the wave; difficult to measure an accurate time when something is moving fast. Suggestions could include using a video camera with a time also displayed.

SP4b.2

1 Your own results.

2 Your own results.

3 You could justify either answer: the wavelength, as this is obtained from a static measurement of the rod; the frequency, as this is measured electronically.

4 Your own table.

5 The sound travels too fast to use a stop clock/human reaction time would introduce errors greater than the time being measured.

Exam-style questions

1 speed $= \frac{660\,\text{m}}{2\,\text{s}} = 330$ m/s (1 for substitution, 1 for evaluation)

2 wavelength $= \frac{1482\,\text{m}}{\text{s}/100\,\text{Hz}} = 148.2$ m (1 for substitution, 1 for evaluation)

3 Use a stop clock to find how long it takes one wave to go from one buoy to the other (1), and calculate the speed by dividing 20 m by the measured time (1).

4 The speed of sound in a metal is much higher than in air (1), and the time between a sound being made and its echo reaching the end of a rod is too short to be measured using a stop clock (1).

SP5a

1 Your own table.

2 Your own graph.

3 Your own results.

4 Your own results.

5 Your own conclusion.

6 a Your own results.

  b Your own results.

Exam-style questions

1 Light travels more slowly/at a different speed in glass (1).

2 a Graph with sensible scales on axes (1) and axes labelled (1) All points correctly plotted to ± half a square (2) *Only 1 mark if one point plotted in error, 0 marks if more than one error.* Smooth curve passing through all the points (1).

b The angle of refraction increases as the angle of incidence increases (1), but the angle of refraction is always less than the angle of incidence (1). The relationship between the angles of incidence and refraction is not a linear/proportional relationship (1).

c The answer should be 9.5° (from the values supplied for plotting the graph), accept ± 1° (1).

3 The student may not have measured the angles accurately/may not have drawn the normal correctly (1).

SP5g

1 Results table complete.

2 Graphs should show curved lines with the gradient reducing as the temperature drops.

3 The rate of cooling gets less as the temperature drops.

4 You should have concluded that tubes covered with dark, dull materials are better at emitting radiation than those covered in light or shiny materials. Your answers should relate the emission of radiation to the cooling rates shown on your graph.

5 Your answers should discuss any anomalous (strange or unexpected) readings and how much difference in cooling rate there is between the different tubes.

6 No, only four different materials have been tested.

Exam-style questions

1 Infrared (1).

2 The wavelength of the radiation emitted by a body depends on its temperature (1) and the water is not hot enough to emit radiation at visible wavelengths (1).

3 a It suggests that dark surfaces absorb more radiation than lighter ones (1) as soot is darker than ice and sooty ice must be absorbing more energy if it is melting faster (1).

  b Light coloured surfaces appear lighter because they reflect more of the visible light that falls on them (1). This means they may also reflect more infrared wavelengths (1). If they reflect more they must absorb less (1).

SP10e

1 A completed results table for both resistor and filament lamp.

2 The scatter diagram should show a straight line through the origin for the resistor, although a curve will be seen if the wires in the experiment got hot. There should be a curve (the slope of the line becoming shallower at higher potential difference values) for the filament lamp.

3 a The values for the resistor require the table to be read accurately and the values obtained substituted into the resistance equation correctly.

  b The values for the filament lamp require the table to be read accurately and the values obtained substituted into the resistance equation correctly.

  c As the potential difference increases, the resistance of the resistor stays the same – but the resistance of the filament lamp increases with increasing potential difference.

  d The scatter diagram for the resistor is a straight line through the origin, which means that current is proportional to potential difference and so the resistance is the same for all values of potential difference. You may also refer to the resistance calculations you carried out for 1 V and 6 V power pack settings. The scatter diagram for the filament lamp shows that the current is not proportional to the potential difference. As the potential difference increases, the current does increase but the change in current gets less and less for each increase in potential difference. This shows that the resistance increases as the potential difference increases.

4 a This is your own opinion as to how close your points are to your line of best fit.

  b The answers should refer to better quality data producing points that lie close to the line of best fit.

5 This is your own opinion as to how reproducible your results were. You need to compare with at least three other groups before coming to a final conclusion.

6 a In circuit Y the ammeter reading will be constant but in circuit Z the ammeters will measure different current values.

b In circuit Y the voltmeter readings V1 and V2 will sum to the value of V3. In circuit Z the voltmeter readings V5 and V6 will be the same as V4.

7 Completed results table.

8 a The current through each filament lamp in parallel should be twice the current measured in circuit B.

b The potential difference across each filament lamp in parallel should be twice the potential difference across each lamp when they are in series.

9 Increasing the potential difference across the supply changes the resistance of the filament lamps. This should not affect how the potential differences across the circuits compare, but may mean that the current through A3 and A4 is twice that of A1 only for lower potential difference settings, and is less than twice A1 at higher potential difference settings.

10 If fixed resistors are used, changing the potential difference across each circuit should not affect the comparisons, because the resistance does not change with potential difference.

Exam-style questions

1 Ohms (or Ω) (1).

2 a Both should be 0.23 A (1) because the current is the same everywhere in a series circuit (1).

b 0.82 A (1) because the current through the power pack/cell is the sum of the currents in the branches of the circuit (1).

3 a i $R = 4\,V$ (1)   **ii** $R = 4\,V$ (1)
       $0.23\,A = 17.4\,\Omega$ (1) $0.82\,A = 4.9\,\Omega$ (1)

b Connect them in parallel (1).

SP14a

1 Your own results.

2 Your own results.

3 Your own results.

4 Your own results.

5 a and b The range of densities for the solids tested is likely to have been greater than the range of densities for the liquids.

6 The answer depends on the materials tested. Answers could point out that in general, solids are more dense than liquids, although there are some solids that are less dense. Very good answers may also suggest whether each solid will float or sink in the different liquids tested.

Exam-style questions

1 a density = $\dfrac{\text{mass}}{\text{volume}}$ (or $\rho = m/V$) (1)

b mass in kg, volume in m^3, density in kg/m^3 (accept g/cm^3) (all three correct for 1 mark)

2 46 g = 0.046 kg (1)
density = 0.046 kg/0.000 05 m^3 (1) = 920 kg/m^3 (1)

3 volume = 2 m × 0.5 m × 0.02 m = 0.02 m^3 (1)
density = 2 kg/0.02 m^3 (1) = 600 kg/m^3 (1)

4 a The measured mass was too low **or** the measured volume was too high (1) ('a measurement error' is not an acceptable answer).

b Any sensible suggestion, such as: use a measuring cylinder with more accurate markings; zero the balance with the measuring cylinder on it and pour the liquid into that, so no liquid is left behind in the measuring cylinder (1).

SP14c.1

1 Your own results.

2 Graphs should show an increase in temperature, a horizontal section while the ice is melting, and then a further rise in temperature as the water begins to warm up.

3 Description will depend on your own results.

4 As the ice is heated the particles move faster and the temperature rises. Eventually the temperature reaches the melting point of the substance and the energy from the water bath is being used to break the bonds holding the particles together in the solid. The temperature remains constant while this is happening. When all the ice has melted, the particles in the liquid move around faster as they get more energy, so the temperature rises again.

5 a Sources of systematic errors could be a faulty thermometer, or the thermometer not immersed fully in the substance being tested.

b Check the thermometer against a known pair of temperatures (e.g. in ice and in boiling water), or compare it with another thermometer.

6 a Suggestions could include not reading the thermometer at the correct time, not recording the reading correctly, or using the thermometer incorrectly (e.g. by taking it out of the substance to read the temperature).

b Answers depend on the errors suggested in 6a. Any sensible methods of reducing errors are acceptable.

Exam-style questions

1 a Ice is a solid, so the particles are held in a fixed arrangement (1) by strong forces (1).

b Any two from: the forces between particles are not as strong as in ice/a solid (1) so the particles can move around (1) within the liquid (1).

2 Graph with sensible scales on axes (1) and axes labelled (1). All points correctly plotted to ± half a square (2). Only 1 mark if one point plotted in error, 0 marks if more than one error. Smooth curve passing through all the points (1).

SP14c.2

1 Your own results.

2 Your own results.

3 Your own results.

4 Your own results.

5 To stop the polystyrene cup falling over.

6 Polystyrene is a better insulating material than glass, so less energy from the warm water will be transferred to the surroundings.

7 The beaker would have allowed more energy from the water to be transferred to the surroundings, so it would look as if more energy was needed to raise the temperature of the water, and the value of the specific heat capacity calculated would be too high.

8 Suggestions for systematic errors could include a faulty thermometer, balance or joulemeter. Suggestions for random errors include not reading the instruments correctly.

Exam-style questions

1 Specific heat capacity is the amount of energy needed to raise the temperature of 1 kg of a substance by 1 °C (1).

2 a 4400 J/kg/°C (3).

b Heat lost to the surroundings during the experiment (1) would increase energy required to raise the temperature of the water (1) so the calculated value for the specific heat capacity would be too high (1).

c Increase insulation to reduce heat loss (1).

SP15b

1 Your own results.

2 Your own results.

3 Answer will depend on your springs.

4 Your own results.

5 The springs with the largest spring constants should feel the stiffest.

6 Your own results.

Exam-style questions

1 a The force needed to stretch a spring increases as the spring is extended (1), so there is not just one value of force that can be used (or similar explanation) (1).

b spring constant = 20 N/0.5 m = 40 N/m (1 mark for substitution, 1 mark for evaluation).
energy transferred = $0.5 \times 40\,N/m \times (0.5\,m)^2 = 5\,J$ (1 mark for substitution, 1 mark for evaluation)

2 a If the total extension is 1 cm, the change with each weight added will be very small (1), and it will be difficult to get an accurate measurement of the extension for each weight (1). (Similar explanations are acceptable.)

b Use heavier weights (1), so the total extension is greater (1).

Practical skills sheet

Tick each technique when you cover them in your practical work.

Biology

Practical skill covered	Core practical	SB1b	SB1g	SB1h	SB1b	SB1f	SB1h	SB1i	SB5k	SB6b	SB8e	SB9c
B1 Use of appropriate apparatus to make a record a range of measurements accurately, including length, area, mass, time, temperature, volume of liquids and gases, and pH												
B2 Safe use of appropriate heating devices and techniques, including use of a Bunsen burner and a water bath or electric heater												
B3 Use of appropriate apparatus and techniques for the observation and measurement of biological changes and/or processes												
B4 Safe and ethical use of living organisms (plants or animals) to measure physiological functions and responses to the environment												
B5 Measurement of rates of reaction by a variety of methods including production of gas, uptake of water and colour change of indicator												
B6 Applications of appropriate sampling techniques to investigate the distribution and abundance of organisms in an ecosystem via direct use in the field												
B7 Use of appropriate apparatus, techniques and magnification, including microscopes, to make observations of biological specimens and produce labelled scientific drawings												

Chemistry

Practical skill covered	Core practical	SC2d	SC8c	SC8d	SC2d	SC8c	SC8d	SC10a	SC14d	SC18b	SC23b	SC25c
C1 Use of appropriate apparatus to make a record a range of measurements accurately, including mass, time, temperature, and volume of liquids and gases												
C2 Safe use of appropriate heating devices and techniques, including use of a Bunsen burner and a water bath or electric heater												
C3 Use of appropriate apparatus and techniques for conducting and monitoring chemical reactions, including appropriate reagents and/or techniques for the measurement of pH in different situations												
C4 Safe use of a range of equipment to purify and/or separate chemical mixtures, including evaporation, filtration, crystallisation, chromatography and distillation												
C5 Making and recording of appropriate observations during chemical reactions including changes in temperature and the measurement of rates of reaction by a variety of methods such as production of gas and colour change												
C6 Safe use and careful handling of gases, liquids and solids, including careful mixing of reagents under controlled conditions, using appropriate apparatus to explore chemical changes and/or products												
C7 Use of appropriate apparatus and techniques to draw, set up and use electrochemical cells for separation and production of elements and compounds												

Physics

Practical skill covered	Core practical	SP2d	SP4b	SP5a	SP2d	SP4b	SP5a	SP5g	SP10e	SP14a	SP14c	SP15b
P1 Use of appropriate apparatus to make a record a range of measurements accurately, including length, area, mass, time, volume and temperature. Use of such measurements to determine densities of solid or liquid objects												
P2 Use of appropriate apparatus to measure and observe the effects of forces including the extension of springs												
P3 Use of appropriate apparatus and techniques for measuring motion, including determination of speed and rate of change of speed (acceleration/deceleration)												
P4 Making observations of waves in fluids and solids to identify the suitability of apparatus to measure speed/frequency/wavelength. Making observations of the effects of the interaction of the electromagnetic waves with matter												
P5 Safe use of appropriate apparatus in a range of contexts to measure energy changes/transfers and associated values such as work done												
P6 Use of appropriate apparatus to measure current, potential difference (voltage) and resistance, and to explore the characteristics of a variety of circuit elements												
P7 Use of circuit diagrams to construct and check series and parallel circuits including a variety of common circuit elements												